# THE RICHARD MATTHEWMAN

# The
# Richard Matthewman
# Stories

## Ian McMillan & Martyn Wiley

POMONA

A Pomona Book

P - 0 1 8

Published by Pomona Books 2009
PO Box 50, Hebden Bridge, West Yorkshire HX7 8WA, England, UK
Telephone 01422 846900 · e-mail admin@pomonauk.co.uk

www.pomonauk.co.uk

1

A CIP catalogue record for this book
is available from the British Library

ISBN-10: 1-904590-21-7

ISBN-13: 978-1-904590-21-7

Cover and back jacket designed
by Andy Martin; thank you.

Set in 12 on 15pt Linotype Magoo by Christian Brett
Printed and bound in England by CPI Cox & Wyman, Reading, RG1 8EX

# Contents

# Foreword

These stories were originally written to be performed on radio. More than that, they were written for a particular actor we all knew, Fine Time Fontayne, who hailed from Wombwell and had a reputation as a strong regional voice in theatre and television. We recorded them in Manchester and they went out on Radio 4 to critical acclaim. Later they went into Radio 4's speech archive and sold as a double cassette. Later still, Fine Time learned every one by heart and performed them round village halls and arts venues; he still does and is bookable as I write. They are unashamedly northern, local, and what you might call, broad. There was already a vital tradition for this kind of writing, subject matter, and style when these were written in the early 1990s and it is one that is still alive today. It focuses on a place, and a people, and around their work and family life. It's funny but also poignant, nostalgic and lyrical. And although it feels more and more to be about times and places and lives now lost forever, somehow it still feels fresh and familiar and true.

Dave Sheasby
Producer, Radio 4

# Preface:
# Lake Darbegon Days

So much of the genesis of the Richard Matthewman Stories is lost in what lesser writers than me would call the mists of history; so much of it is tied up in that strange Land that Time Forgot known as the late 1980s; so much of it involves my old bedroom at home and my mother struggling upstairs with a tray of tea and slices of parkin. So let's take this preface with a pinch of salt, let's not bother checking the dates because many of them will be inaccurate.

This morning, on my way back from GT News in Darfield, walking past the Maurice Dobson Memorial Museum that features as Harry and Jud's shop in the stories, I tried to ring Dave Sheasby, the producer of the stories on Radio 4, to see if he could sort out the chronology of them and the other things we were writing at the time, but he was out. Typical. Freda Jobling walked past me as I was ringing him and said:

"When I got up this morning I couldn't walk on this leg."

I smiled and nodded.

So, during the late 1980s me and my pal and brother-in-law Martyn Wiley had made a couple of series for Radio 4 called *Hearing Voices, Seeing Things*. They were little 15 minute programmes focusing on neglected jobs, hidden corners of the North, with sounds recorded on location and poetic scripts that tried to bring out the hidden life of the subjects.

I did an after-dinner speech in Mexborough recently and an optician collared me:

"You made a programme about me on the radio!" he said.

I'd forgotten, but it was true. *Hearing Voices, Seeing Things: The Optician*. He'd taped it and he quoted the opening to me: 'A small, neat man ...' He liked that, he said. A small, neat man. Well, he was.

The programmes were really about mythologising South Yorkshire at a time, just after the miners' strike, when it was in danger of falling apart.

Another of the *Hearing Voices, Seeing Things* programmes featured a walk down to Houghton Main pit with an old councillor. As he wheezed his way back to his house he bumped into his mate George (Bertha Jobling's husband, as it happens, dead these last many years) and they both looked to the sky and said, as one, 'Utopia, kid!'

Martyn and I had lived in Darfield all our lives and we had a fund of stories about a place that had often seemed far from the centre of things and, at one of our endless meetings with Dave Sheasby in The Broomhill Tavern in Sheffield thrashing out ideas for the next offers round, we came up with the idea of 'Lake Darbegon Days', a version of Garrison Keiller's *Lake Wobegon Days* in which he told stories of a small American community that somehow, despite their inconsequentiality, took on a kind of majesty in that American way. We'd tell tales about Darfield.

At around the same time (I told you the chronology was hazy) Dave, Martyn and I were writing a radio comedy series called *The Blackburn Files*, and that's where my old bedroom comes in. *The Blackburn Files* was set in our familiar South Yorkshire territory: it was about a miner, Stephen J. Blackburn, who had been made redundant from the pit and was setting himself up as a detective. We wrote the pieces with the Wombwell (next place to Darfield and equally mythological: ask about the drummer who played *Skin Deep* and went on too long and got chucked out of the plate-glass window of the Prince of Wales) actor Fine Time Fontaine (not his real name) who understood the particular language of the Dearne Valley and knew that, when the wind was in the right direction, you could spot somebody from Goldthorpe by the way they pronounced 'door'.

We'd sit in my old bedroom at 13 Edderthorpe Lane, Dave hunched over the typewriter and me and Martyn pacing about eating parkin and coming up with gags and Dave, because he had the typewriter, deciding which gags stayed in. He who has the means of production has the power. It still rankles that my 'He didn't know anything about country music; he thought Willie Nelson was a wrestling hold' gag never got to see the light of day. Until now.

Martyn and I decided that the *Lake Darbegon Days* programmes should be read by Finetyme because he'd get the rhythm right. We then started telling each other tales from our shared childhood and it occurred to us that we were fictionalising them just a bit. Just a little, little bit. Did that really happen at that time? Did he really say that then? Wouldn't it be funnier if she said that just as he went out of the room? Would that hat be funnier than that hat? We discovered, as all fictioneers do, that writing is editing and reinvention and that autobiography is memory plus fireworks.

So *Lake Darbegon* became *Richard Matthewman*, and *Richard Matthewman* became one-third me and one-third Martyn. And one-third somebody new. We shared the writing but sometimes one or the other would take the lead, would type while the other paced and parkinned.

The stories are exaggerations of things that actually happened, like my tale of learning to drive or Martyn's visit to the clothes shop on the day England won the World Cup. They feel personal and universal at the same time, and maybe that's why, at least once a month, somebody comes up to me at a gig or e-mails me or writes to me or rings me up to tell me how much they love them, and so it's lovely to welcome all the stories into print.

Martyn died in 1994 and this book is dedicated to his memory and all the times we laughed till we cried.

Ian McMillan, Spring 2009

# The
# Richard Matthewman
# Stories

# Whatever Happened to Freddie Galloway?

It was 1962, and I was in Mrs Hudson's class at Low Valley Juniors. It was Monday morning, it was raining and it was the day the school photographer came. My mam stood there with the rain-mate in her hand, and I stood there sobbing.

"I'll look daft in a rain-mate," I said, my breath coming in great heaving gulps. "I'll look like a lass."

My mam wasn't impressed.

"You'll not look like a lass! How can you look like a lass with knees like that?"

She arranged my hair one last time and placed the rain-mate carefully over it.

"You are not going to look like Alfalfa for your school photo. You are not going to sit on Auntie Mabel's mantel-piece like a scarecrow!"

All the relatives got my school photo for an additional Christmas present—me smiling out in front rooms from the borders of Scotland to the North Derbyshire coalfield. I had the kind of hair that stuck up like a brush, so on the weekend before the photos I always had to go to Mad

Geoff's for my hair cut. I never fathomed why they called him Mad Geoff, except that he always wore a dicky-bow which I suppose sets you apart in a village like ours.

I'd gone after school on the Friday night. Mad Geoff's was empty except for Bing, sitting there in his trilby and serenading us with *Three Coins in The Fountain*. When we came in, Bing stopped singing and, looking at my mother, said to Geoff:

"Has tha gow owt for't weekend?"

And Geoff said:

"Aye, a country cottage."

My mam stared into space.

When I got into the chair, Geoff said:

"What does tha want then, Richard? Tony Curtis? Dickie Valentine? Fabian? Elvis?"

I was about to say Fabian when my mother said:

"He wants a light trim, Mad. An extremely light trim."

Geoff was famous for his enthusiastic cutting. Anything other than a light trim came out like what my dad called a barrack room special.

As Geoff trimmed and his clippers buzzed I heard Bing telling my mam about The Daz Man.

"They reckon they'll be coming round this area next week, Mrs M, so you'd better keep your eye open for 'em."

"They'll not be coming round here,' said my mam scornfully. "The rent man's the only that comes round here."

"Well, you'd better have your packet of Daz ready,

Missus," Bing piped up. "If you complete that slogan they'll give you a ten-bob note."

Geoff just missed my ear with his clippers:

"Aye, and if you believe that you'll stand for't egg under't cap." He then whipped the sheet off me and said:

"Does tha want any jollop on it?"

I was about to say yes when my mam said:

"He does not! It took two days to wash it out last time!"

"Who's the Daz Man, mam?' I asked as we walked home through the park.

"It's just some daft stuff off the telly. Some soft articles who come knocking on your door because they've got nowt better to do.'

Now it was Monday morning and I was walking to school in the rain with a rain-mate on. I tried to hide behind my mam as we caught up with Robert Doughty. If he saw me in a rain-mate he'd never let me forget it. As we drew level with Mrs Doughty and Robert my mam turned to me in triumph.

"There, Richard. I told you it was a good idea."

There was Robert Doughty, the cock of class six, with a rain-mate on. A pink rain-mate. He looked at me with murder in his eyes. In the cloakroom my mam took the rain-mate off and folded it up. She patted my hair nervously.

"What time's the photographer coming, anyway?" she asked.

"Two o'clock, Mrs Matthewman,' said Robert, still with his rain-mate on. He looked like a sea anemone.

"Two o'clock?' said my mam to me in horror. "How are you going to keep your hair tidy till two o'clock?"

"I'll make sure Richard keeps his rain-mate on,' said Robert, angelically.

Assembly was taken by Miss Parkin. We sang *When a Knight Won his Spurs*, said some prayers and then Miss Parkin looked at us and said:

"Well, I can see you've all remembered that the school photographer is coming today. And this year we're going to try something a little bit different. As well as the individual photos, we're going to do some class photographs. That means in years to come, when you're all big boys and girls, you'll be able to look at the pictures with fond memories. Now, who knows what fond memories are?"

A forest of hands shot up, mainly from the younger infants. Miss Parkin pointed to Mary Till, who was straining her arm upwards and snapping her fingers enthusiastically.

"Yes, Mary. What are fond memories?"

Mary looked doubtful.

"Fond memories, Mary. Do you know what we mean when we say fond memories?"

"Seven," said Mary.

"That's nearly right, Mary. Have another go. Fond memories."

"Seventy-ten,' said Mary, triumphantly.

4

Miss Parkin signalled to Mrs Hinchcliffe to begin the music, and we filed out to Ravel's *Bolero*.

Everybody was excited about the photographer coming. We'd all come in our best clothes, and at least five lads in our class had been brought to school with rain-mates on. Mrs Hudson said that we all looked a picture already and Noel Ramsden said we looked like fond memories and Mrs Hudson smiled and gave him a star.

At playtime Mrs Hudson warned us: no running about, no fighting, no donkey rides, no football. Robert Doughty came up.

"Where's your rain-mate, Richard? I promised your mam you'd wear it."

I tried to ignore him. The rain-mate was in my pocket. Robert walked right up to me, pressing himself against me.

"I said, where's your rain-mate? You've got to wear your rain-mate or your dad'll get his belt out. I heard your mam tell my mam. Get your rain-mate on."

I felt the tears welling up in my eyes.

"It's not raining," I said, quietly.

"Put it on anyway or I'll squeeze your balloons."

I didn't know what that meant but it sounded painful. I got the rain-mate out and put it on. Everybody laughed. The tears splashed down my cheeks. Mrs Robinson came out and rang the bell, and we all lined up. Everybody was looking at me. Mrs Robinson said:

"You can take your rain-mate off now, Richard, but that's a very sensible boy for putting it on."

I wiped my eyes with my cuff and allowed myself a little smile.

We'd just started back after play when a big boy came round with a note. Mrs Hudson read it and said:

"Will you all stop what you're doing, please. Now."

We all sat quietly and looked at Mrs Hudson. She had bright red lips which were famous throughout the school. In those days most teachers didn't wear lipstick and if they did it was something pale and subtle. Not Mrs Hudson: she lit the classroom up like a beacon as she welcomed us each morning. And now those bright red lips were pursed like she didn't understand the message the big boy had brought.

"This note has just come round from Miss Parkin, and it's very serious so I want you all to pay attention."

She read it carefully:

"There are some people in the village with a doz hats but you are on no account to take one of them if offered."

Mrs Hudson put the note down and looked at us.

"Doz. That's a dozen."

She looked at me.

"How many hats is a dozen, Richard?"

"Daz hats," I said. I felt like Mary Till.

"Yes, all right. How many is a doz?"

"They're Daz hats, Mrs Hudson," said Freddie Galloway.

"I know there's a doz, Freddie, but how many is that?"

I could see that Mrs Hudson was getting exasperated. She'd moved from the Forest of Dean when her hus-

6

band's pit shut and sometimes she couldn't understand a word we said.

"It's Daz, like off the telly, Miss," said Freddie. "Blokes are coming round and if you get words reight they gi thi a big hat. It's only for a laugh."

Mrs Hudson looked more puzzled than ever. She folded the note up and put it on her desk.

"Anyway, Class Six: these people need their hats. You are not to take one. Now get on with your poems about 'My Favourite Feeling,'."

Dinner-time came round quickly. I gobbled my dinner down and went out to play. The weather was still dismal. The supply teacher from Huddersfield was bundled up in scarves and a big fawn duffel coat. We called him Green 'Un because he looked just like the man from the Sue Ryder Home who sold the Green 'Un outside Harry and Jud's shop on a Saturday afternoon.

I wandered up to the gate and looked out. The pit bus went past taking the afternoon shift, and I waved to my dad. He didn't wave back, just sat there staring into space.

Behind the pit bus was a brightly coloured van that looked like a packet of soap powder, driven by a man in a white trilby. It was the Daz Hats! The van stopped outside the gates and the man got out. Word spread instantly and loads of us crowded round the gate.

"Who'd like a hat? Anybody like a hat?"

We were hesitant at first, then Noel Ramsden said:

"I'll have one!"

The man put his hand into a bag and pulled out a big

blue hat with, 'WASHES WHITER' on it. Noel put it on and we all laughed. Noel said:

"I don't know the slogan."

And the man said:

"It doesn't matter, kid. It doesn't matter. Let's just get rid of some of these bloody hats!"

We all recoiled a bit at the rude word but then surged forward when he started to pull hats out of the bag. I got one: it was too big and it flopped over my ears but it didn't seem to matter. We were all running about and laughing. Bill Lillee had two hats on, and Robert Doughty was throwing his up in the air and catching it. Suddenly we all went quiet. Miss Parkin was standing there, her face pale with fury.

"What do you think you are doing, Keith Barlow?' she said to the man with the hats. He looked sheepish.

"Just giving out these hats, like, for a joke Miss Parkin."

"You've been in the George by the state of you, as well. You've not changed since I used to teach you, Keith Barlow, you've not changed a bit. Now get away and take those silly hats with you.'

He climbed into the van and drove off. We were very impressed by the fact that Miss Parkin seemed to know everybody in the world. She turned her anger on us:

"I'm surprised at you, I really am. Now give me those ridiculous hats and you can go back to your classrooms because the photographer will be here in a minute. Fond memories, children, remember? Fond memories."

I passed her my hat but I was surprised to see that some

people were taking a huge risk by stuffing theirs into their pockets or down their jumpers. One fell on the floor and Miss Parkin picked it up with a smile. We filed into the classroom.

Mrs Hudson licked her finger and smoothed my hair down as we queued up to go to the photographer. She smiled at me and I smiled back. The photographer had a little horse puppet and he shouted, 'Watch the Horsey!' to make us look happy on the picture. After all the individual ones were done, we had a group one together for the class photo. The little ones sat at the front and I stood at the back with the other big lads. I had Robert Doughty on one side and Freddie Galloway on the other.

Once the photographer had us all settled, he waggled the horse puppet and shouted, 'Watch the Horsey!' and at that moment lots of things happened at once.

Freddie Galloway pulled a Daz hat out of his pocket and put it on and at the same time Robert Doughty fished one out of his cardigan and jammed it on my head. Miss Parkin ran across the room like she was being chased and the camera flashed. I'll always remember that moment, and what it led to: Robert and Freddie being sent home, and the start of Freddie's long decline that ended in 1991 when the pit shut and he took to wandering between the George, the Sportsman and the Drop through the long afternoons.

When Miss Parkin died, her sister came to see me. I'd just started teaching and I was doing some work at the kitchen table. She came in and said:

"Miss Parkin wanted you to have this; she always knew you'd amount to something.'

It was the picture. Me with the hat crushed on my head, Robert Doughty looking wicked, and Freddie Galloway smiling innocently beneath his big blue brim. Washes Whiter. Fond Memories.

# Harry, Jud, Kennedy
# and Me

It was 1963, November, Friday night, CLB night —
Church Lad's Brigade. Six till eight in the church hall. I'd
been going for six months. I'd creak down the stairs at ten
to six after a cat lick with the Imperial Leather, kiss me
mam, salute me dad and strut off down the yard like a
South American General: blue tunic, red tie, chip bag hat
under my epaulet and a stripe down me trousers. I'd
climb over the wall, nip down the back of Edward Street
and out into the dimly lit space of Morrison Road. Then
I'd go and call for my best mate, Henry Ford. That really
was his name; his dad was mad on rugby league, you see.
You always had to knock for a long time at Henry's
house, because their Jed was practising *Trumpet Tune and
Air* on his cornet in the room.

Their house was just like ours really: terrace row, front
door opening onto the street, back door onto the yard, two
up, two down, toilet across the way and no bathroom.
Anyway, I'd knock for Henry for what felt like an hour
and I'd hear his mam's voice struggling against the
draught excluder, Persil and badly fitted teeth, yelling:

"You have to come to't back, love."

Henry's older sister, Maureen, would be standing at the top of their steps carefully lowering a vivid blonde bee-hive under the lintel. Behind her I'd catch a glimpse of Mr Ford's shoulders pumping away as he worked steadily on his own coiffeur in front of an oval mirror on the chimney breast. His suit trousers, like chest waders, would be hanging dangerously close to the fire. Henry's mam would call him from upstairs, 'HENRY' and he'd come clattering down in his church lad's uniform. Well, just the tie at that stage. He was hoping for a cap and a tunic that night. As we left the house Mr Ford would always shout:

"H'up, two, three, four. H'up, two, three, four. Quick, march."

This would always make Mrs Ford laugh coarsely, then, falling into a loose cough, she would crawl to the fireplace, part her husband's trouser legs like a stage curtain and spit mightily into the flames.

Me and Henry set off. Halfway down their yard he said:

"Watch out for that brassiere, it's Mrs Pitchford's."

He was a couple of seconds too late. Then out into Church Street and down the hill towards the church hall. We passed a building site opposite the council offices, which our teacher, Mrs Roach, had told us was going to be a library. We passed the police station with the old air-raid siren on the roof and the haunted cells. We passed Dr Walker's house, with the tin hut surgery in the garden where everybody's mam went for thick orange juice in brown bottles on a Thursday and where Henry's dad went for a note for his legendary glass back every Monday.

At the bottom of Church Street we'd nip into Harry's shop for a packet of torpedoes and some Spanish. It was a 'Beer-Off' with a pump on the counter, rows of bottles, and shelves of tin and sweet jars in the window. Harry, immaculate, with a flower in his button-hole, would be carefully arranged on a high stool in front of the counter, smoking a long cigarette. Jud, his partner, stocky, in a brown smock, would be behind the counter and both of them would be talking to Sergeant Blyton. Blyton's helmet would be resting on a shelf next to a stack of Zetter's coupons and a big jar of pineapple chunks.

Harry and Jud. Legends. A couple, they were. You know, like married, to each other. They'd kept the shop for years and, before that, were waiters together in a big hotel in Bournemouth. Some said Jud had been a paratrooper in the war. I tried to imagine his brown smock billowing out over Arnhem. Some said that before the war, Harry and Jud used to wear frocks and lipstick and go for walks down the Pit Lane holding hands. The funny thing was, nobody ever laughed at them. Well, if they did it was only once. Harry had been a good boxer when he was younger and if any of the lads tried it on he'd pull them over the counter and give them a straight left and then finish 'em off with a Senior Service ashtray.

If he knew you went to church, Harry would always try to make you swear. He'd put half a crown on the shiny counter, call for order, and then in a voice lost somewhere between Wilfred Pickles and Kenneth Williams try and cajole you into saying 'bloody'. He'd sit there in his powder blue suit with matching tie and hanky saying:

"Go on. Go on. Say, 'Bloody'. Go on."

And Jud would shake his head and tut and say:

"Leave bairns alone, you silly old chuff," then slip us a handful of Spangles he'd got from the warehouse, loose.

But it didn't happen tonight. They seemed different. More serious. Jud served us. Harry didn't speak and as we were going out I heard Sergeant Blyton saying:

"It's got t'be Russians, Harry. For me, it's got to be."

Church Lad's Brigade, CLB, Church Hall, Friday six till eight. Used to be a cinema, The Empire. It took them two years to convert it, the men of the church. From Frankenstein to CLB. From Gregory Peck to Young Wives. From Betty Grable's legs to a retired bishop giving a talk about his years in Africa, illustrated with slides, and followed by a faith supper. Working parties in overalls, ripping out maroon-velvet seats, knocking up partitions and creating meeting rooms for Sunday school and the Bible class in the old dress circle.

Me and Henry went straight in. We were late by now. Everybody else was in what the men of the church had elected to call, 'The Supper Room'. It always seemed strange to me that, 'The Supper Room'. Supper was a solitary meal that me dad enjoyed after five pints. It was always served on a stool in a darkened room in front of the telly. It always seemed to involve lumps of bread and a sea of dark gravy. At the church hall I'd try and visualise the rector, Mr Short and Mr Wilkinson the church wardens and Frank Brown, the ancient verger, all sitting on a row of kitchen stools, dipping bread at the same time.

Me and Henry dashed in. He was desperate to get that tunic and cap and he knew that points were knocked off for lateness and sloppy dress. Strange thing was nobody seemed to notice. All the other lads were just hanging about, waiting for things to start. The three leaders were huddled in a corner near the serving hatch, looking worried. There was Les Marsden. He was a sergeant, crew-cut like iron filings on a magnet, 20 going on 53, worked at the Drapery Co-op. There was Lieutenant Palmer, John Palmer, of Snydale Road, he worked on the screens at Monkton Number 1. He kept telling the rector that he wanted to leave the NCB and go full time for Jesus and the rector kept advising him to get some O-levels first. So Friday was his only free night, what with all his night-school commitments. Then, there was Mr Kay. Captain Kay. Our leader. He'd been in the war and he was always on about how he'd lost a leg in Burma. They must have found it for him, 'cos he'd always had two since I'd known him. Mind you, he did have a bad limp. Captain Kay hadn't got his uniform on. I think he might have come straight from work. He still had his suit on and a propelling pencil in his pocket.

Captain Kay turned to face us. He cleared his throat and tried to say:

"Right lads, let's get fell in."

But he'd had to have two runs at it and even then his voice were cracking. Y'know, like our Steven's did when the rector asked him to either sing tenor or keep his gob shut and help serve communion.

Captain Kay stood there in his suit, flanked by John Palmer and Les Marsden in their uniforms. Above their heads, on the Supper Room wall, on the framed print of the crucifixion: Jesus and the two robbers. Alan Shaw, of Haverlock Street, had always reckoned the two robbers looked just like Harry and Jud. I'd never noticed it before now, but now I did and wanted to laugh. I imagined them both hanging there, trying to get Jesus to say 'Bloody'. I kept clearing my throat, pressing my cheeks in with my hands and thinking about the death of my grandad's dog, Crips. Captain Kay finally got his voice back and said:

"Right lads, sit down. I've got some very serious news."

At the word 'serious', Les Marsden and John Palmer nodded, and as their heads dipped I caught another glimpse of Harry and Jud hanging in their loincloths. It was too much to bear. I let out a surprisingly loud yelp. Across the room I noticed Eric Snowball's thin shoulders quivering as he fed a large hanky into his mouth. Captain Kay continued, unperturbed.

"Right, sit down, please lads."

This was harder than you might think. The Supper Room doubled as a store room and the only chairs were some green metal ones stacked eight high. Captain Kay continued:

"Tonight, in Dallas, Texas, America ... "

Johnny Singleton snorted and then coughed at the same time. At the back of the room another boy went, 'Hhh,

hhh, hh,' and smacked himself on his lip with his fist.

"Tonight, President Kennedy, whom some of you lads will know from the television, has been shot ... dead."

Billy Gent's stack of chairs slowly collapsed like a felled tree. The captain gave him a hard look. Well a hard look for an insurance man who did youth work. Anyway, the captain glared at Billy and then continued. Over his left shoulder, Les Marsden was smirking. On the other flank John Palmer was carefully considering his shoes.

"We're not yet sure who is responsible but we've got a pretty good idea that it's probably the Russians."

For a second there was complete silence. Then, suddenly, Tony Cartilage leapt from his stack of chairs and ran out of the room. We heard him sprint down the corridor, crash through the double doors and hurl high pitched laughter into the lofty dark of the main hall, formerly the Empire cinema. Others were now giggling openly.

"So, this evening lads, there will be no CLB. There may well be another war, you see."

The poor bloke was so upset that he was talking in poetry. Three more stacks of chairs went over. Henry started to shriek like a Mynah bird. In the main hall Tony Cartilage was on his knees squealing. With a final desperate effort at self-control, John Palmer executed a smart right wheel and smacked the wall behind Captain Kay's head. The picture of the crucifixion slipped. On the other side of Captain Kay, tears were streaming down Les Marsden's wobbling cheeks. Les, always a serious man, was slapping his left thigh in an attempt to regain control of his body and emotions. Only the Captain seemed immune to this strange hysteria.

"So lads, in the event of another war, many of you may well be called upon, with your training and specialist knowledge, to play a part. So what I suggest you do now is get off home, get a good night's sleep and prepare for tomorrow. Good night lads and God bless."

On the words 'God bless' Captain Kay's voice shattered. He began to laugh and the floodgates were flung open. We laughed and laughed. We wept. We fell off our chairs. We clung to each other like wrestlers and stumbled around the room howling. Les Marsden dropped to his knees and started to slap the floor with one of his shoes. High above us, Harry, Jud and Jesus stared impassively.

Slowly, the laughter died. In ones and twos we trudged out into the November night. Me and Henry had nothing left to say. We walked up past Harry and Jud's shop. It was brightly lit and empty. Harry was standing outside, staring up Barnsley Road. I shouted good night to him and he turned and said:

"We've lost a lovely man."

And I saw that his face was wet. It scared me. I left Henry and ran the rest of the way home. I went into the house. Mam and dad were in the other room; I could hear the telly and American voices. I went straight upstairs, into my bedroom where I took my uniform off and threw it on the floor. I never went back to the CLB. I couldn't face Captain Kay and the uniforms. And I didn't want to look at Harry and Jud and Jesus just hanging there. Something changed.

# Kicking Off
# to Grammar School

Banks, Cohen, Wilson, Stiles, Charlton, Moore, Ball, Hurst, Charlton, Hunt and Peters. July 30th, 1966. The day we won the World Cup. We'd just settled down to watch it, me with me air horn off me bike, me dad with his suit and bobble cap and our Shirley laid out on the floor reckoning to read *Fab 208*. Me mam was upstairs rooting in the ottoman.

We kept hearing creaks and thuds in the back bedroom. In fact, at one bit me dad had to shout up to her:

"Will ye gi o'er now!"

Me mam just brayed a couple of times on the floor and then started singing *Glorious Things of Thee are Spoken*, in her best chapel soprano. German national song, me dad reckoned.

They'd just kicked off. It was drizzling and suddenly there she was. Me mam, stood in front of the telly in her best coat and that head scarf me grandma had brought her from Babbacombe. My dad couldn't believe it. He leaned his head back over the settee like I had to do when I had me hair washed over the sink. Then he stretched both his arms up, pointed at the newly anaglyptic ceiling and said:

"Jesus, God Almighty, help me please."

"You," me mam said, ignoring him and pointing at me. "Wash your hands and face and I mean a proper wash and that means ..."

And I had to say ...:

"Soap, mam."

"And give it a good rub with the ..."

"Flannel, mam."

"And wash behind your ..."

"Lugs, mam."

"Ears", bellowed my dad. "Do it reight. Ears. It's bloody ears. With ye lugs. Tha gets lugs on wing nuts."

Me mam just gave him her best 'wither on the vine' look.

"C'mon, we're going out."

"Out? Where to?"

"Town."

"What for?"

"Blazer, flannels, cap, gabardine, tie, shirt, pullovers, rugby kit, boots, shoes, pumps, satchel. I have a list from the council offices."

"Don't forget your woodwork apron," piped up our Shirley from the rug.

"Shift," shouted me dad, slamming his hands down onto his knees.

At that precise moment, West Germany took the lead. My dad slumped forward like he'd been shot in the back.

"But mam, it's World Cup final. We can't go into town, now."

"We can. It'll be nice and quiet. We'll get a seat on the bus."

I considered a final appeal to my dad then thought better of it as he sucked greedily at the third of the line of bottles of pale ale that he had got arranged 4−4−2 on the sideboard. He made impatient gestures with his free hand, like a referee waving play on. I followed me mam into the kitchen where, unable to find a flannel, she attacked my cheeks with a dishcloth.

We did get a seat on the bus, just. It was full of women. One or two kids in my predicament and the most miserable driver I've ever seen.

"How's it going?"

"Fine, thanks."

"Football match. How we doing?"

"We're losing, thank you very much," said me mam and, at this, a group of fat women near the back broke into a round of spontaneous applause.

We sat next to Mrs Beck … it were a squeeze. I was right on the edge of the seat, hanging over the aisle and the conductor clonked me with his ticket machine as he passed. Mrs Beck had a natural curiosity, or as my dad put it 'The longest snout on our street' and she was quickly into her stride.

"I say, your Richard's done well, hasn't he Eileen?"

My mam pursed her lips and gave a slight nod. Her chin dipped and eyes half closed like a broken doll.

"Aye," continued Mrs Beck. "I were only saying to the mester, 'their Richard has done well, considering.' I say, you've done well, Richard, love. Passing up to the grammar school."

And then she leaned across. Horrified that she might try to kiss me, I swayed into the aisle and took another glancing blow from the conductor's machine.

Grammar school. The envelope had come one Saturday morning. A thick brown one, that slapped the mat, stuffed with forms, lists, a map and, of course, the letter:

'Pleased to inform you: Monday September 3rd 10 a.m.'

That had surprised my dad. He started work at 4 a.m. Then he noticed it was just for the first day, thereafter 9 a.m. Nobody in our family had ever been to the grammar school before — in the same way nobody in our family had ever been abroad. Apart from my Uncle Terry's debacle at Monte Casino.

There were four lads in our class who passed: me, Simon Hargreaves, Michael Smith and Lol. His real name was Taj Topolovski, so obviously we called him Lol. His dad was Polish, worked at the sweet factory. He'd been abroad. In fact he still was, in his head. Two girls passed for the high school and the rest, the other 27, were consigned to the Alderman John Turner Secondary Modern School, with the earliest release date of 1971, into the waiting arms of King Coal and the sewing factory.

The bus station was almost deserted. Mrs Beck said:

"I'll have a steady walk with you, shall I? I've got to go to the Co-op, for me new corsets."

I went bright red, thinking of the pictures in me mam's catalogue, pictures of well-groomed women, none of whom resembled Mrs Beck, in corsets, all gazing confidently at something in the distance.

"No, we've to get his pit watch from Rymers," said me mam.

This was news to me.

"I didn't know me dad's watch was broken."

"It isn't. But if you think I'm trailing down Eldon Street with that thing you can neddy. Corsets!"

So then, we couldn't just walk up to the Co-op. We had to go the other way: Market Street, Hill Street, Summer Lane, then down Bugs Alley. Me mam kept sending me on ahead like Tonto to look for a big woman bearing corsets. The coast finally clear, we scuttled into the Co-op via the Chapel of Rest. Then three flights of stairs, a corridor, some fire doors that me mam shouldered open and suddenly there we were: Mens and Boys Department. Hushed under the combined weight of racks of suits and fitted carpets, it was unusually quiet. I didn't know at the time, but England had just equalised. Apparently at this point my dad had shouted:

"Gerrin ye bloody thing, yeah!" and, in his excitement, sprayed half a pint of Magnet pale ale up the chimney-breast. He'd tried to clean it off using a dishcloth, only to succeed in rubbing a hole the shape of Tasmania in the wallpaper under the mirror. In his confusion he'd stepped back, tripped over our Shirley and gone all his length, banging the back of his head on me mam's new hostess trolley. According to our Shirley, he'd laid there laughing. Our Shirley went round Leanne Upperdean's after that to listen to some Swinging Blue Jeans EPs on their Barry's Dansette.

Meanwhile me and me mam got the stuff, everything on the list except the athletics vest. There'd apparently been a run on athletics vests. We must've been in that shop above an hour. Every so often an ancient man in a double-breasted black suit would toil up three flights of stairs from his perch in the electrical goods to relay news of the match. The first time he appeared, Martin Peters had given England the lead. The old man, whose lapel badge announced him as: 'R.T. Mole' and who the assistant serving us told my mam had been on the last boat out of Dunkirk, shouted:

"Peters. Two-one."

Then, just after the woman serving us had wrapped up six pairs of grey socks with blue hoops, long woollen, Mole surfaced again. Blinking, he said with quiet dignity:

"Ladies and Gentlemen, I regret to inform you that the Bosch have equalised through Herr Weber."

Struggling under tons of flannel, we staggered out into the late afternoon sunshine and Mrs Beck, with her unmentionables in a tartan bag.

"All fixed up are we? Kitted out? Got your athletics vest?"

My mam pursed her lips, kissing the air like it was the cold cheek of a dead relative. At that moment a party of people in wheelchairs from Newport House parked in front of a flickering monochrome wall of DER, Bush and Murphy screens broke into a ragged cheer. Without moving her head, Mrs Beck said:

"Hurst. Three two. Disputed Russian linesman. Tash on like our Bill."

We finally shook her off at the corner of Peel Square. We did a smart right wheel up a snicket, leaving Mrs Beck talking to nothing. Then me mother said:

"Right, just one more job for you, laddo."

"Oh, mam."

"Don't 'oh mam' me."

And with that she pushed me into a phone box, pulling the heavy door closed behind her, trapping us both inside.

"You, my lad, are going to learn how to use this," she said, tapping the heavy Bakelite instrument with its braided cord.

"But mam ... "

"No arguments."

"Why?"

"If ever you're stuck after school, in town, miss your bus, going to be late, all you have to do is use this."

"This?"

"Yes."

"But mam, who shall I ring?"

"Don't be stupid — me."

"But mam, we're not on the phone."

"Granted," she said, unflustered.

"What you'll have to do is ring Renee Tunstall."

"Not Renee Tunstall," I said.

"She's got a phone."

"She's also got a 'tash."

"Shut it and don't be so damned ignorant."

My mam searched her handbag, then pulled out a postcard and four pennies. She said in a voice, suddenly serious:

"Now then Richard, always, and I mean always, keep these with you."

I nodded.

"For emergencies and I mean emergencies. This money could be your lifeline."

The four old pennies felt big and hot as they clinked in my hand.

"If ever you're stuck, come into one of these, pick up the phone, put your four pennies in there and dial Renee's number. Now do it."

"But what shall I say, mam?"

"I've written it down for you Richard, on the back of that card. Now, when Renee answers just read the message, she'll understand and she'll fetch someone."

I picked up the phone. It weighed a ton. I dialled. You had to wait ages for the dial to return before you could do the next number. At last it started ringing. It seemed to ring for hours. Finally, a reply. I slammed my hand into button A and the pennies dropped with a clatter.

"Hello," said a gruff baritone.

Funny how people sound different on the phone. I started to read from my mam's card.

"Hello, Renee Tunstall, can you hear me? This is Richard Matthewman, Eileen's lad."

The baritone interrupted.

"I think lad's got wrong number, cock."

Thinking this was part of the test, I started to read the message again.

"Hello, Renee Tunstall, can you hear me? This is …"

The voice cut in, sharper this time.

"Ahh well, this isn't. Bugger off.".

"Well?" said me mam

"Er … wrong number."

"What?"

"It were misters, swearing and that."

"That's four pence gone, Richard. You can forget next week's *Valiant*. I'll dial it."

She did. It rang. Four more pennies dropped. A voice. Renee. The phone handed back. The message held in front of my sweating face.

"Hello, Renee Tunstall, can you hear me? This is Richard Matthewman, Eileen's lad, off the top street. I am unavoidably detanned."

"Detained," hissed me mam.

"Detained in town. Please will you ask my mam or dad to come to the phone, at once. Sorry to ring but it is an emergency."

There was a perplexed silence, so I started again. She interrupted quickly.

"Hang on Richard, I'll see what I can do."

My mother nodded. There was a long pause. Then the sound of approaching footsteps down a passage. Then the sound of something breaking. Me dad's voice metallic, distant, saying:

"Hellfire, sorry missus, I'll get ye another."

Then ...

"Hello?"

"Hello, dad. It's me."

"How's thi mean?"

"It's me. I'm ringing up for a practise, like."

"For a what?"

"For when I'm at grammar."

Then the pips went and at that moment, as me dad swept up the fragments of a Stafford pot dog and me and me mam shouldered into Eldon Street, Geoff Hurst ran half the length of the pitch and made it four–two. They think it's all over. It is now.

# The Summer of Love, tha Knows.

They called it 'The Summer of Love', nineteen sixty something. All over the world, lads my age were rolling about in fields with girls, going to pop festivals, wearing beads, growing their hair and saying things like 'Hey man, far out.' I'd seen them on the news being led away smiling by grim coppers and me dad would say, 'Look at state of that thing. They want shooting, the lot of them,' and me mam would sigh and say, 'It's the mothers I feel sorry for,' and I'd sit wondering if the summer of love would ever get to Barnsley.

I'd suddenly gone all gangly and my voice had finally broken, well, shattered. For weeks, every time I spoke, I sounded like Tarzan swinging from a tree. I'd started experimenting with my dad's razor and spending hours in the bathroom, where I'd take tentative puffs on Embassy Tips I'd found in the kitchen drawer. I remember, one night, I sat on the toilet like I'd seen Americans sit on chairs, you know, the wrong way round. I sat there, facing the cistern, with the window wide open. I'd borrowed my dad's lighter and I kept fiddling with it, not quite knowing how it worked until, suddenly, a massive flame shot up, leaving a terrible smell of burning and petrol and terror.

"Richard, what the bloody hell are thi doing in there?"

"Nowt dad, nowt!"

"Is there summat afire?"

"Er … no, no. It's bonfire smoke from them allotments, dad."

"Ah, well, make sure thi gets an early neet. You're working in morning, don't forget."

Holiday job. Labouring for the council. Five weeks at 12 quid a week, and no tax. There were eight of us. Students they called us. And the funny thing was, I was the only one who wasn't related to someone on the council. There was Andrew Watson and his brother David and then there was Chris and Steve Watson, they were cousins. There was Kevin Dowd, his dad was on the County Council; Michael Lee whose dad was Clerk to the Council; Colin Foster, his dad was Housing Manager; and me.

The first day was strange. It was the last Monday in July, pouring with rain and the letter I'd had from Michael Lee's dad had said that I should report to the council to start work at 7.30 a.m. By about quarter to eight all the other student workers had arrived, but there was no sign of the full-timers. Then, just before eight, a very old van, with the Council crest — cross shovels and a teapot — painted on the side, sped into the yard, skidded to a halt and spat out Billy McNeil, the foreman. Everyone knew Billy. He was five one, Scottish and had the shortest fuse in South Yorkshire.

"Who the hell are thow?" raged Billy. Twenty years in Barnsley had done odd things to his accent.

"Students."

"Students? What the hell are you lot doing in my yard?"

"Reporting," said Colin Foster.

"For work," I chipped in.

"First I've heard. There'll be hell to pay over this when the Union finds out."

"My dad said that it'd be alright," Mike Lee piped up.

"Hooo, did he now, did he indeed? And who might your papa be, ey? Sir Alex Douglas chuffing Hume, is it?

"No, it's Alf Lee, you know, the Clerk to the Council."

A sudden change came over Billy.

"Alf Lee, a marvellous man. Oh you should have said son, you should've said. Standing out here in the rain. Come in, come in. Get yourselves into the Snap Cabin. I did nee recognise you, lad. How's that lawn we put down for your dad?"

"Fine, thanks."

"And the decorating?"

"Lovely."

Then he went, leaving eight of us in a bare room with benches around the outside and an old stove in the middle, a pin-up from October '64 on one wall and a vast sagging armchair in the corner. My working life had begun.

The full-timers started to arrive. Most of them were familiar faces. Many of them were called Watson or had married Watsons. Then there was Alan Blake, council

33

plumber, burst pipes a speciality; he was very short sighted. And Len Walton, the legendary council lorry driver, who none of us had ever seen anywhere other than behind his wheel and were amazed to find was six foot six.

At exactly two minutes past nine, a taxi pulled into the yard and an enormous fat man in a suit got out and, without paying the driver, lumbered into the mess room. He flopped into the big chair where, closing his eyes, he said:

"Right, you chappies."

At which, everyone ran for the door. Apart from young Alan Blake who, kneeling down, eased off the big man's shiny shoes, carefully replaced them with tartan zip up slippers before tiptoeing to the door.

"Who's that?" I asked a passing Watson when we got outside.

"Big Mal."

"Who's Big Mal?"

"Don't ask."

Outside in the yard, Billy McNeil stood in immaculately pressed overalls, shouting. Apparently at the sky.

"Eight. Eight of the chuffers. What the hell's name can I do with eight of them?"

Colin Foster, the Housing Manager's son, piped up:

"Should we come back next week?"

"Tha soft in the bonce son or what?"

Young Alan popped his head round the cabin door and said:

"Plant pots."

"Tha what?"

"Big Mal says put them on plant pots."

Billy smiled.

"Great idea, plant pots, great."

So began three weeks of sitting in a shed with no windows, washing ten thousand plant pots in buckets of cold water with a balding toothbrush, as, one-by-one, all the other lads were assigned to better jobs. The Watsons all got what Billy called 'light duties'. These included going to the shop for cigs and cleaning councillors' cars.

Poor old Colin Foster was picked out for what the foreman called 'special duties'. Sadly, Colin seemed proud of this and spent the whole of one day asking round the yard for a left-handed socket set and a bucket of compressed air. The other men cottoned on and Colin spent days seeking a glass hammer and long weight. So that left me and Kevin Dowd. After the first day the weather changed into what Billy McNeil called a 'topical heat wave'. He'd walk round the yard saying, 'Topical innit. Bloody topical. Better than Girvan.' But there was no sunshine for me and Dowdy. Day after day as the shed got hotter and the smell of creosote and soil grew sicklier, we sat there under a 60-watt bulb, sweating and scrubbing like forgotten prisoners in a far away country. So we talked for hours about the others, Big Mal and Billy McNeil. We laughed at Colin Foster and his endless search for compressed air and glass hammers.

"Always Colin, int it?"

"Yeah, well."

"Even here they get on at him."

"Well it's only a laugh, int it? No harm done."

But even as I said it, I knew that neither of us really believed it. It had always been the same; Colin was too trusting. He always believed everything everyone told him. At infant school it was the ghost in the toilet. In the juniors it was the wild dog on the allotments and the note we made him take round saying the Easter holiday had been extended to eight weeks, for which Mr Owen, the head, had given Colin the slipper. Somehow, it had always seemed alright to laugh at Colin — before we went to the grammar school.

He was one of us, but at the grammar it was different. There was lads from the town and all the other villages and suddenly he wasn't our Colin anymore but public property, the butt of everybody's jokes. On the first day, he actually slipped on a banana skin in full view of 200 lads in blazers. Later that morning, in our first assembly, Colin stood up in the middle of *He Who Would Valiant Be*, walked to the front, and, as the singing died away, announced to the whole school that he had a dog called Bess. After that, he had no chance.

By the end of the second year, just saying his name could reduce a whole class to tears of laughter. His name entered the language as an insult. People would say, 'You great Colin' or sometimes, 'What a Foster!' We were usually in different classes, so I didn't feel too responsible for what happened to him. There was one terrible day in third-year, when a big lad that we all knew as Animal told Colin that he needed his help with a project on the suffragettes. Colin, of course, believed him and spent the next five hours chained to railings in a far place near the rugby field. And whenever teachers said, 'Anyone seen anything of Foster?' none of us spoke. The fire brigade brought him back at ten past three, in chains.

The fourth-year field trip was worse. To this day, I still squirm just to think about it. Twenty-six lads, two Geography teachers and a bus driven by a bloke called Stan who confided to me on the first evening that he was being followed by the Russians, everywhere.

"They're after me, kid. They're after me. Thee watch, I'll be lucky to see the week out."

Shropshire it was. We descended on Church Stretton like locusts and within two hours there wasn't a pair of sunglasses to be had in the whole town. Meanwhile, 26 of us strode through drizzle on the Long Mynd in gleaming Polaroids, our pockets stuffed with stolen Mars Bars. Colin got lost. Though to be honest, he did have help. Somebody told him that field trips had to have a scout like on *Wagon Train*, and sent him off into the mist with a broken compass. But, sat now in our steaming shed, with our buckets of cold water and toothbrushes, it was the coach journey home that Kevin and me remembered most of all.

"We should have told Avery sooner, shouldn't we?"

"What?"

We'd just refilled our buckets and were carrying yet another tray of dirty plant pots over to the bench where we were working.

"Yeah, we went too far."

Motorway services, near Leicester. We'd stopped briefly and as we chugged slowly away, with Stan quietly weeping (as he had been for the past two days), Mr Avery had shouted, 'Are we all here?' and someone had called back, 'Foster's not all here, sir' which brought a ragged round of applause. At this, Mr Avery—who had a degree from Cambridge, wore a bow tie and prayed to God every night that he might die before the school went Comprehensive—slumped into his seat saying, 'Drive on, driver.' But Colin wasn't on the bus. Even as we passed signs for Heanor, Hucknall and Derby, Colin was trying without success to release himself from a toilet cubicle at Leicester Forest, where someone had managed to lock him in, with the help of a Swiss Army Knife and some lies. Near Chesterfield, I cracked. It had gone very quiet on the bus and, feeling sick, I walked to the front and said, 'Sir, Foster's not here.'

"What?"

"Foster, sir. He's not on the bus. We think. We think, he might still be at Leicester, sir."

We spent the next three hours on the hard shoulder. Phone calls were made, the police came and went and Stan finally left us, sobbing, in an ambulance, with a blanket around his shoulders. Eventually Mr Avery took the wheel saying, 'I served in Spain, you know' and we set off home. Even at that moment, Colin's dad was suspending an important council meeting, so that he could drive over 200 miles to release his hapless son from a toilet in Leicester. Later, in the privacy of their elegant Victorian, villa-style house, he would beat Colin with the stick normally reserved for the dog.

The next day was terrible. I was singled out in assembly and praised for my, 'Prompt action and consideration for others.' Then, at break, Colin came up to me and said:

"Thanks Richard, for getting me rescued yesterday. Me dad says to tell you that he can get you a summer job on the council if you want.'

"Oh, alright then. Thanks, Colin."

And, all the time, my Swiss Army Knife felt like it was burning a hole in my blazer pocket. Burning a hole right through into my skin.

# A Long Day's Leaving

There's no doubt, looking back, that it was one of the longest days of my life. There hadn't been that many really long days up to then. Two or three, perhaps.

One was the time we broke down on the way to Bridlington and had to spend a long hot Saturday in a lay-by just beyond Goole. We were in a van that me dad had borrowed from a mate at work. It was a Bedford with sliding doors. Just after Thorne, me dad, who was sweating like an Alabama cop, had slid back his door to get some air. The door had kept on sliding and crashed to the ground, narrowly missing an old man on a black bike. It took an hour to get the door back on and me dad got some oil all down the side of his new holiday trousers. That was a long day. I think what put the tin hat on it for me mam though was arriving at the Parkhurst Guest House in the middle of the evening meal and having to troop through the dining room with two kids, three cases and a husband who looked like he'd just done a double 'un down the pit. I can still remember the faces of the family from Ossett as they all paused, spoons of tomato soup halfway to their open mouths.

The Bridlington incident was almost as long a day as

Christmas Day 1962, when I put all the clocks in our house forward three hours so I would get my presents quicker. We were the only family in the village to have our Christmas dinner at ten o'clock in the morning.

Long days. Christmas 1962. Bridlington. And then, the day I left home. October 4th 1973. The day I went to University. I had waited a long time for that day to arrive. In fact I'd waited all my life, I suppose. Nobody in our family had stayed on at school after the age of 14 before I came along and then suddenly there I was, grammar school, O Levels, A levels, interviews, offers, brown envelopes, lists and a date: October 4th, fixed in everybody's head.

Me mam predictably went crackers with excitement. She insisted on issuing what amounted to a press release to both the *South Yorkshire Times* and the *Barnsley Chronicle*. She knew this woman at the Co-op Women's Guild who was the local correspondent at both papers. My embarrassment was total when I found almost half a column devoted to this hot news, plus a blurred picture taken at Filey three years earlier that made me look like that lad off the front of *Mad*. What made it worse was the story came out in both papers on different weeks, with an interesting range of typographical errors. In the *South Yorkshire Times* I was: Richard Matthews, age 18, and having gained 30 A Levels and succeeded in gaining a place at … gaining a place at … Gunning the University of College. Whereas the *Chron* got it more or less right until they revealed I was eight years old.

I think me dad was quite pleased about me going to University. He never said much, really. He'd make jokes about it being better than having to work for a living. But I do remember one Sunday night though, about a fortnight before I was due to go. He came in from the pub and we were sitting in the kitchen together while he had his supper. He was big on his meal and gravy supper, me dad. Anyway, he'd had a few pints and it was a warm evening. We had the back door open. There was a big moon over Murdoch Street and we were both sweating.

"Not long now, lad."

"No, dad."

"Ah."

"Two weeks."

"Ah. Cut us another slice of bread, will thi?"

"Ah."

"Looking forward to it, Richard?"

"I think so."

"Think so?"

"Well yes, I suppose."

"Ah. Well I'll tell thi summat now. Ye keep up wi it, wi ye studying, right?"

"Yes."

"Make sure thi does. Ye don't want to end up like me."

"But dad ..."

"Any more gravy?"

I think that was the longest conversation we'd ever had. I knew as soon as he asked for more gravy that he'd said what he'd wanted to say. So we both went quiet, thinking, sat either side of a red Formica table, with the big moon and the warm night looking in at us.

Just two other things I remember most clearly about that summer were the shopping trips my mother dragged me out on, and the question of hair. It was 1973. Everyone had long hair. Footballers, news readers, middle aged reps, even clergymen. Everyone's ears and shirt collars disappeared. Everyone's except mine. I was determined not to go to university with naked ears and my mam was equally determined that my hair should be kept in what she always called 'a proper style'. That is: shaved neck and a side parting kept in place with a handful of Brylcreem. We had more arguments about this than I care to recall and by the time October arrived my hair had mutated into a bizarre hybrid that reflected elements of Oscar Wilde and mid-period Cliff Richard.

October 4th 1973. It was sunny. It was actually quite hot. It was also probably the last time in my life that my mother decided what I was going to wear. I think we probably both knew, so I didn't protest too much. Anyway, I knew it was the first and last time I would wear the outfit we'd bought together at the Co-op in July. It was the same place we'd bought my uniform for the grammar school seven years previously and I think my mam had this idea that there was a uniform for universities as well and that Kingsley Amis had invented it between dashing off chapters of *Lucky Jim* sometime in the mid-1950s.

Imagine the picture: me, me mam and our old fella,

climbing into a maroon Mark I Cortina Estate that burn-
ed oil in clouds. Two suitcases and a duffel bag in the
back. Me mam in a hat, me dad uncomfortable in a flapping suit, tight white collar and tie, and me in a shrieking
sports jacket, bottle green stay-pressed flares and my
mam's one concession—a yellow paisley shirt with
matching tie. The neighbours had seen nothing like it
since Mavis Bisby's wedding and didn't bother twitching
the curtains but simply came out onto their steps and
gawped with pleasure. I blushed and tried to crouch
down in the back. My dad cursed softly but fluently as he
edged the car down into Edward Street and my mother
sat, impassive, hat fixed on newly permed hair, gazing at
the distant horizons way beyond back yards and wet
washdays. After we'd gone about ten miles she turned to
me dad and said:

"You'd think Maureen Cooper would do something
about those teeth, wouldn't you? I mean, they can do
marvellous things these days and well, they're so ..." She
paused considering the possibilities. "Well they're so un-
sightly aren't they?"

"Uh," me dad replied. "She looks like someone's
smacked her wi house brick."

"And if her Arthur gets much bigger," my mam
continued.

"No be reight, that's glandular, that is," put in me dad.

"Glandular? It's beer, more like. He never misses a
session."

Then turning to me, she said:

45

"Never mind, Richard, you'll be going to a better place, love."

I just smiled weakly; more convinced than ever that being taken to university by your mam and dad wasn't quite what you were suppose to do.

The journey should've taken about two hours. In took nearer four. We spent an hour and a half touring the back streets of Leicester searching for my hall of residence. We asked passers by for directions on several occasions and once there was almost an incident between my dad and a local man, who, as it turned out was deaf, but who my dad was convinced was being, 'bloody ignorant'. He was all for getting out of the car and, as he put it, 'lamping him one'. Then the car started to overheat and we had to spend 20 minutes in a particularly leafy avenue with the bonnet up and me and me dad just stood there like failed game show hosts, whilst me mam remained impassive, staring ahead.

It was early afternoon when my dad finally berthed the old Cortina between a pearl grey Mercedes and a British racing green Jag on a sea of expensive sounding gravel. For a minute we all sat in silence listening to the car ticking as various bits of it cooled off. Then me mam opened her handbag and took out a packet of mints. We all took one and then solemnly passed them on. It was like communion. All of us waiting, smiling, trying not to move our jaws or be the first to shift in our seats. I think, looking back, all three of us were terrified. Suddenly there was a tapping on the window next to my mam. We all swivelled round like gun turrets to see a pair of piercing green eyes set in a tropical forest of hair, framed by the collar of an Afghan coat, from which hung a large cross on a chain. The undergrowth parted and a surprisingly light coloured voice struggled out.

"Hi folks. Er, greetings, ma'am."

My mother looked stunned.

"Ohh, hello," she said.

My dad recoiled in horror, breathing out the single phrase 'hellfire'. All the things he'd read in his papers and heard in the Cross Keys about students and taxpayers' money confirmed in a single glimpse.

"Look at the state of that thing," he said.

But me mam sounded uncertain, bewildered. Clinging to some wreckage in her head, she added the words:

"He's very well-spoken, anyway."

At that moment, I wanted to cry. We weren't a family that went in for emotion or touching normally, but just then I wanted to put my arms around me mam and dad and say, 'Don't worry, it'll be alright' and I wanted to tell them how much I loved them and it was because of them that I'd got this far. If this was far. Which I now know it wasn't and that they were as good if not better than all those Jags and Mercs and lads with daft jackets. But me being me and them being them, I think I said something like, 'Right, best get out then' and we did and then we all crunched along a gravel path like contestants in a particular bizarre *It's A Knockout* game. The long haired one leading, talking with his hands about 'A' Block, senior common rooms and refectories, me in my new sports jacket and a suitcase that suddenly looked shoddy, then my mother carefully carrying a handbag like it was a bomb. She said to me dad:

"They keep the grass nice, don't they?" as he sweated under the weight of a suitcase full of books and a green tartan duffel bag. Then doors, steps, corridors with floors that squeaked under our shoes and a room, a bathroom. The long haired one retreating with the words:

"Okay folks, leave you to it. If you need anything, anything at all, man, just give me a shout, right?"

"Er, yeah, ta, pal mate, like," I petered out.

Then the door slammed shut. Simultaneously, the door of my empty wardrobe swung open and 17 wire coat hangers jangled a mournful tune.

I'll always remember the last bit. Me mam wanted to unpack for me. I didn't want her to. Me dad said, 'leave lad alone' and turned and smacked his head on an unshaded blue light bulb left by the previous occupant.

The room was too small for us. It ended up with me perched on the bed like a recovering patient, me mam in what passed for an easy chair and me dad seated, for the only time in his life, at a desk. We didn't say any more. We all knew that as soon as they went, that would be it. Me gone. Left home and I wouldn't be back or if I was it would never be the same. Could never be the same. We walked back to the car in our silly clothes. Somewhere from an open window there was music playing loud. It was Crosby, Stills, Nash and Young singing, 'Our house is a very very very fine house, with two cats in the yard,' and at the car, my mother pressed five pounds into me hand and my dad sat for a minute at the wheel with the engine running, knowing that he should say something. Something that would help.

In the end, he said:

"Remember Richard, mind you leave the bathroom as you find it, right."

"Right."

Then he blew his nose on a vast white flag, spun the wheels on the gravel and was gone, trailing blue smoke that drifted away over the striped lawns.

# Grisp the Wheel at Ten Past Two

The car horn hooted outside. I didn't move. I stood looking at myself in the mirror. The spot on my neck was huge. Vesuvius, the kids at school called it. I'd been teaching there two terms. The longest two terms of my life. September 1977 to April 1978. Then, sitting on the bus on the way home the other night, a gang of big women from the tennis-ball factory got on. They always got on at that time. They smelled of rubber and scent, and they took over the bus. One sat next to me. She stared at my neck. I felt myself getting red. The woman in front was showing the woman next to her photos of the Queen Mother's recent visit to Barnsley.

"That's her hand, waving," she was saying. "Eee, hasn't she got lovely gloves on!"

I tried to lean over to see the pictures and the woman next to me said:

"What's that on your neck?"

The two women in front turned round slowly. My neck was more interesting than the Queen Mother's gloves, waving. I stood up and got off the bus, a mile before the house.

The horn hooted again. I went outside. The driving instructor's car was white, and not as new as it could have been. 'Don's Driving School,' it said on top. Don himself sat inside. He was a small, balding man, and I noticed that he was wearing the biggest pair of sandals I'd ever seen. He looked at me, then looked at my neck, and sucked in his breath.

"I don't get many your age," he said. "It's mainly kids, just past their 17th birthday. It's mainly kids."

All my mates in the lower-sixth had got driving lessons for their 17th birthday. Dave Sunderland had got a car. It sat in the drive as he took lesson after lesson and failed test after test. He washed it every Sunday and always sent for the AA road maps for his holiday with his mam, and then sat studying them on the coach as the car gathered rust and a cat had kittens underneath it. Eventually he passed and drove to the shop in triumph for his mother's regular order of Advocaat. And that left only me. I once asked a girl out, in that summer after I left school and before I went to college. I said I'd meet her at the bus stop opposite the cemetery. She looked at me with withering contempt and said, 'You can't be a man with a ticket in your hand.' Her parents got the *Manchester Guardian* and she was going to Arts College in Falmouth.

Don shifted his sandals and looked at me again and said:

"Not many your age. Like I say, not many your age."

"Well, I'm fed up of the bus," I said. "Slow, over-crowded, and I've to wait in the bus station for another one. Two buses to catch, an hour and 40 minutes door-to-door and it's only eight miles."

"I bet kids on the bus take the Michael out of that thing on your neck and all," he said. "I bet kids on the bus take the Michael."

He drove us to a lay-by just outside the village. We changed places. As I got out I noticed that his sandals flapped like flippers.

"Right. Comfortable?"

"Er...yes."

"Okay. This is the brake. This is the clutch. This is the accelerator."

My neck was killing me; a heavy, continual pain that made it hard to grasp what he was saying.

"I said, turn it on. Use the key. Turn it on, using the key."

I almost said, 'No, I've changed my mind,' and got out and walked away. I didn't really want to learn to drive. I enjoyed being in cars, enjoyed being a passenger, but being a driver, in charge of a lethal machine that could kill and maim, no thanks. But I thought about the bus station in February and the factory women and the bloke with the stick who always saw me on the bus and made a point of sitting next to me and showing me the scars on his back, and I turned the engine on and tried to proceed into traffic, as I'd seen my dad do many, many times.

The car leaped forward like a kangaroo and there was a terrible crashing of gears. Don grabbed the wheel from me and a huge articulated lorry went past, blaring its horn. Don was white and sweating. I thought driving instructors were meant to be calm.

"Bloody hell fire! I mean, bloody hell fire! What were you trying to do? Kill us both? We'd have ended up looking like that thing on your neck if that artic had flattened us. That thing on your neck."

I noticed that when Don got agitated he repeated things even more.

Somehow we got into the stream of traffic and crawled down the road. Don was a bit calmer, although a twitch had started ticking away under his left eye. I hunched over the wheel like a cop in *Highway Patrol*.

"Relax," said Don. "Relax. Relax."

I tried to relax.

"You're not holding the wheel properly. You're not holding it properly. You've got to grisp the wheel at ten past two."

"Don't you mean grip the wheel at ten to two?"

Don's twitch went into top gear.

"Grisp it, grisp it. Grisp the wheel at ten past two. Grisp the wheel at ten past two!"

I grisped it, both hands round the right side of the wheel, and he slapped my hand.

"Like this, like this!" he said, holding his hands up in the ten-to-two position.

We drove on. I stalled at traffic lights, drove in first gear. I felt my collar chafing at my neck. The hour was almost over.

"Turn left up this hill," said Don. "Turn left up this hill. Turn left up this hill."

I turned left. Snape Hill, very steep indeed. The car juddered and began to lose power.

"Change gear. Change gear. Change gear. Change gear," said Don, his twitch dancing madly under his eye.

I was in second gear and the hill was too steep. I needed to get into first. I changed gear. Into fourth. The gearbox almost exploded and the gearstick leaped out of my hand. The car stopped. A bread van almost crashed into us, and then swerved by, the driver gesturing a two finger salute with the fingers spread very wide and the hand going up and down very slowly. It made me think of the Queen Mother's gloved hand and I had to stifle a giggle. I coughed.

"It's not funny. It's not funny. This car is my living. My living."

"I'm sorry."

"Well, be more careful. Be more bloody careful."

We got slowly to the top of the hill. Don wiped his face with a big hanky.

"Slow down here. Pull in here."

"What for?"

"Just slow down here. Pull in here. Pull in here."

The car ground to a halt outside the Methodist chapel. On the notice board there was a poster which said, 'Well Done is Better Than Well Said'.

"I won't be a minute," said Don, clambering out of the car, sandals flapping.

I wound the window down and leaned out.

"Why, where are you going?"

"I've got to get some sticks," he said.

At least that's what I think he said. He went round the back of the chapel. I sat there in the pale sun and felt the thing on my neck. It hurt. It was sort of soft round the bottom and then hard round the top. Like a nipple. After a while I noticed a woman looking at me through the open window. It was the woman who'd sat next to me on the bus.

"You want to see a doctor with that," she said.

I tried to look away, as though I'd got something phenomenally interesting in the glove box. Her eyes bored into my neck.

"My uncle had one of them. The doctor had to clean it out with a wire."

I couldn't stand it anymore. Where the hell was Don? I got out of the car. Where was Don going to get sticks in a chapel? The side door of the chapel was open, so I went in. The room felt cool and smelled of polish. I could hear a voice muttering at the far end of the big room. It was Don. He was standing in the pulpit reading something, but I could hardly hear him. I walked down the aisle towards him. An old lady in a big blue hat looked at me and smiled. I noticed that someone was lying in one of the pews, asleep. It was Phil Allsop, the Methodist Sunday school leader. As I looked at him, he woke up. I went to school with Phil; he was always a bit holy. He once told Mr Drinkwater that he should take Jesus into his life and Mr Drinkwater clipped him round the head with a hardback copy of *The White Company* by Sir Arthur Conan Doyle. Phil sat up, rubbing his eyes. He looked exhausted.

He worked in the offices at the bed factory because his mother used to say he was delicate. I noticed that he deliberately wasn't looking at the thing on my neck.

"All right, Richard. It's good to see you in the house of the Lord. What brings you here?'

"I'm looking for Don. I'm supposed to be having a driving lesson with him."

Phil looked distressed.

"Well, that's just not fair. He told me he'd cleared his diary. We're only up to Numbers as well."

I was baffled.

"I'm sorry, but I don't know what you're talking about."

"I did the whole night-shift. Bill Ellis was supposed to do the four a.m. section but glory knows where he got to … I had to do all night on my own and now I don't know if I'm coming or going. And Don was meant to do three hours this morning and he was almost an hour late. It's just not on!"

He sounded close to tears.

"I still don't know what you're on about," I said.

Phil looked at me as though he was seeing me for the first time. His eyes were almost shutting as he spoke.

"I'm sorry. I'm so tied up in this thing. It's to raise funds for the Sunday School outing. We're having a sponsored neck reading."

"Pardon?"

"A sponsored bible reading. The whole lot from Genesis to Revelation. Should take about four days altogether. We're supposed to do two-hour shifts but I've been quite badly let down by my volunteers.'

"You said sponsored neck reading."

Further down the church, in the pulpit, Don stopped muttering and shouted:

"I won't be a minute. I'll just get to the end of this chapter. I'll just get to the end of this chapter."

Phil turned to him in despair.

"Oh, Don! Can't you stay another hour? I've got Violet Mullis coming at twelve. Her sister's bringing her from the home."

"I can't. I can't. I've got to get Stirling Moss here home and then I've got another lesson with him that won the pools. I've got to get Stirling Moss here home and then I've got another lesson with him that won the pools."

He put his head down and carried on muttering, turning a page. Phil sat down heavily; he looked older, somehow. In fact he looked the spitting image of photographs I'd seen of his Grandad Allsop in the trenches. It must have been the quality of light in the chapel. I know one thing — my neck was giving me hell.

"Don't worry about it, Phil," I said. "I'll get the bus home. I don't think me and driving are meant for each other."

I felt in my pocket and gave him some change. More than I intended, actually.

"Here, have this for the Sunday School outing."

He smiled, and the years seemed to fall away from him. He looked at the money and I remembered that after Mr Drinkwater had hit him with the copy of *The White Company* Phil had smiled and said, 'I forgive you, Mr Drinkwater, you didn't know what you were doing.' So Mr Drinkwater hit him again with Lamb's *Tales of Shakespeare*. Maybe he'd end up a saint. Phil, not Mr Drinkwater.

Phil looked at the money.

"Well, every bit helps," he said. "But we've a long way to go before we reach our neck."

I went outside before I hit him. I knew how Mr Drinkwater felt. The sun had gone in and it was blowing cold. The old lady in the big blue hat followed me out; she reached over and touched me on the arm.

"That thing on your neck," she said, in a thin, quavering voice. "My late, dear husband had one in the fifties. Around the time the first sputnik destroyed the weather. I rubbed it with lard every night. That got rid of it. Try it. Try lard. Only the best lard, of course."

She turned and went back into the chapel.

Lard! What a stupid idea. I walked down the street to the bus stop, then turned round and went to the shop on the corner. I looked at the lard, smug in its tight white packets. I caught sight of my reflection in the shop window. The thing on my neck looked like as big as a satsuma. I picked up a packet of lard and took it to the till.

"What's that thing on your neck?" the lad behind the counter said, as he put my lard in a carrier.

"Just give me the lard," I said. "Just give me the lard. Just give me the lard."

# A New Suit and a
# Sit Down Tea

"He's still stuck," said me mother.

She was trying to fasten my top button at the time. I was red in the face and I felt like I'd been hung. I had difficultly breathing.

"You've got a neck like a bloody toilet bowl," she said.

It was a nice image, a sort of untutored simile. It was my wedding day. She stopped fiddling with the button. I held up a brown kipper tie.

"This'll cover it up," I said. "Nobody'll notice."

"I'll notice," she said, flicking her hair out of her eye like she did when she was agitated.

I could tell she was dying for a Park Drive but she'd given them up. There were stacks of mints in the pantry and her teeth were rotting away and she'd put on half a stone, but at least she'd given up smoking. I'd started. Well I started at college, really. Late night parties, passing round joints. I didn't at first — I told them I was on antibiotics. I told them I'd got a cut lip and mouth ulcers. I told them me dad once set me hair on fire knocking the stuff out of his pipe when he was on a ladder freeing a great bustard from the newly painted upstairs window sills, where it'd got its feet stuck. They laughed and said I didn't need drugs. My mind was far away, anyway. And it must have been true because when I tried the drugs I just went cross-eyed and vomited on a youth from Burton-on-Trent. We kept in touch for a while after he left. I thought of inviting him to the wedding but I never got round to it.

My dad came in, in a vivid blue suit.

"He's still stuck," he said.

"Last time it happened, he were like it for three weeks, Yarmouth."

My mother flicked her hair. It was my cousin Bill they were talking about. Big Billy Boy, 23 stone, worked down the pit for three days, didn't like it, said he had back trouble. Nobody believed him for years and then a couple of months after England lost to Brazil in the World Cup Quarter Finals his back went when he was brushing his teeth, bent over in agony. Now it happened every so often and it had happened in our bathroom doorway. I could tell me mother was close to tears.

"Can't you and Harry just manhandle the fat bugger out of the way? I've got to get in there to get my outfit on, me hair done. Our Richard's got to brush his teeth."

My dad put his arm around her awkwardly.

"It can't be done, love. He says his vertebrae might crinkle up."

The room was getting smaller. I felt claustrophobic.

"I'll go and have a word with him," I said.

I went across the landing to the bathroom door. There was Bill, bent double in the doorway, his face puce.

"Y'alright then, kid?" he gasped.

"Not bad, how yore?"

"Well I'm alright on me'sen but me back's giving me some cosh."

"Can you move at all? Just a little bit to let folks get through to the bathroom?"

"No chance. Doctor says if I try to force it, I'll end up in a chair for rest of me life. Can't risk that."

He was naked from the waist up. He'd been getting a good wash and the rolls of fat hung over his trousers. His breasts were huge and pendulous and the nipples had little tufts of obscene wiry black hair around them. Perhaps if I plucked one of the hairs out he'd straighten up.

"Where you going for yer honeymoon then, eh?"

"The honeymoon was spent at the couple's new home," I replied.

It was going to be true. 26 Henry Street, a mid terrace, near the bus garage. Seven thousand quid and the previous owners had taken everything. Even the light bulbs and the door hinges. That's the only thing that rhymes with orange, door hinge. We had this tutor at college, funny thing, he was called Mr Tewta and he took us for English. He was obsessed with poetry. *The Possibilities of Rhyme* — that was the name of the book he'd published in the 1960s. He loved rhyme. He said it was the basis of all art. I didn't know what he was on about. We made up a limerick about him and left it on his desk.

> "There was an old fella called Tewta,
> Who had an enormous hooter,
> He liked to rhyme,
> All the bleeding time,
> And had a brain like a computer."

He didn't get mad. He seemed to like it. It was the last class before the Christmas holidays and he said:

"I'm going to set you a challenge to wile away the hours between the turkey and the Christmas pudding. See if you can find a rhyme for orange."

He laughed wickedly. It came to me on the train home, just popped into me head: door hinge. It was a bit of a cheat really, particularly because around our way they said 'dour inge' but it seemed to fit. You should've seen his face when I told him. I let him build it up at first. It was a cold morning in mid-January and he spent ages wiping his glasses with a bit of rag.

"Now," he said, like I bet he did every year.

"Has anyone been able to solve my little er … conundrum. Can anyone tell me what might possibly rhyme with orange?"

He looked around the class. Nobody caught his eye. I let it go for almost too long and then I said, 'Door hinge' very clearly. There was a long silence. It was a wonderful few seconds.

I'd wanted to go somewhere exotic for the honeymoon. Magaluf maybe or the Orkneys but Lindsay reckoned we couldn't afford it.

"We can have a good time at home," she said, putting on her sex kitten face.

I'd always found her sexy, except when she was trying to be sexy. I don't know if she thought I was sexy, she never told me. We'd met in the staffroom at St John's J and I. I was the lowest of the low, a probationary teacher, and she was on supply for Mrs Cadwell, whose nerves drove her and her husband to drink. I fancied her straight away. We went out together and now, here we were, about to get married and I couldn't fasten me shirt and our Bill was bent over in our bathroom doorway like a sumo wrestler in suit trousers. It wasn't going to be an auspicious start.

It was going to be different to me mam and dad's wedding. Teddy boy job, that was. They kept all the photos in a biscuit tin and we used to get them out every so often and giggle at them. We once had a power cut halfway through a viewing and me dad reckoned it was Buddy Holly switching the lights out. I didn't know what he was on about. Me dad looked amazing on the pictures, drainpipe trousers, thin string tie and a quiff you could've sliced Hovis with. Me mam just looked very embarrassed; she's looking down at her white shoes most of the time. She looks lovely though. I never think of me mam as beautiful except on them wedding photos. They had a big reception in the upstairs room of The Cross Keys. Big Jim Shelley drove them to Cleethorpes in his Cadillac with tin cans tied to the back all the way and then they had my Uncle Albert's caravan on South Beach for a whole week. Me mam says they used to go out and watch the trawlers going into Grimsby and then they'd walk into Cleethorpes and go round all the pubs until they ended up in The Dolphin, where they had a group who were called, with stunning originality, Ready Teddy Go.

"They were rubbish," me dad used to say as we gazed at the photos in the biscuit tin. "Just three deck hands with amplifiers."

Big Jim Shelley loved that Cadillac. He was the only bloke in Barnsley with one. He crashed it in the late 1960s, when he'd had one too many and he lost the use of his legs. He ended up sitting in a chair all day and the Cadillac rusted away in his front garden.

I went back in the bedroom. Me mam was puffing away on one of our Bill's Wills' Whiffs. She threw it out of the bedroom window when I came in, but the room still smelled like Christmas.

"He can't shift," I said. "He's stuck."

She shook her head in disbelief.

"We'll have to work round him," she said.

I went downstairs. Me dad sat there in his blue suit. When it had come from the makers he'd gasped at it.

"It's bloody blue, that," he said. "It's bloody blue."

"Any progress with mighty Joe Young?" he said, gesturing upwards with his thumb.

"Still stuck," I replied.

I stood there in the middle of the room, not knowing what to do. I didn't really feel excited or scared or anything. I know I should've been excited. A new decade, a new job starting after the six-week holiday at Beely J and I, with my probation year done, a new wife, a new house, all these new things. It should've been like Christmas, but it felt more like the day after Boxing Day. Flat and empty. Lindsay's house would've been full to bursting; aunties, bridesmaids, my sister among them, pageboys, those mysterious relatives that nobody ever seems to know. But our house was quiet. Dead quiet. Me dad in his blue suit, me mam puffing a wiff, our Bill in the bathroom, me downstairs and Malcolm. Where the hell was Malcolm?

"Where the 'ell's Malcolm?" said me dad.

I shook me head. It had been one of Malcolm's endearing traits at college, always late for everything. Just like his excessive drinking and fast driving were endearing. Now I just wanted him to be here with the rings in his pocket and his tie on.

"He's been gone for hours," said dad.

His suit had epaulletes at the shoulders.

"He was only popping out for some confetti from Harry and Jud's, where the 'ell can he be?"

I sat heavily on the settee next to me dad. Upstairs I could hear me mam trying to get Bill to move. We sat in silence. Upstairs, Bill groaned. Me dad farted. I could tell that he'd been trying to do it quietly, raising one of his buttocks off the settee, but it hadn't worked. Neither of us said anything. The phone rang, it was Malcolm.

"I'm in Rotherham," he said.

"Rotherham? What the 'ell for?"

"Remember Debbie from college? She lived in

67

Rotherham, didn't she? Well I thought it'd be a laugh to invite her to the wedding. Ridge Road wasn't it, her address? I'm just on my way up there now. Won't be long, I'll be back with you in half an hour, with Debbie I hope."

"It wasn't Rotherham, it was Rotherhithe. Ridge Road, Rotherhithe," I told him.

"Ohh, God, so it was."

"And the wedding's in half an hour, so get back here quick."

"Don't panic, they can't start without us."

I turned to me dad.

"He'll not be long," I said. "He's in Rotherham."

Me dad didn't say anything.

"Is there owt on telly?" I said, trying to take his mind off things.

I switched on. It was a Tarzan film. He was swinging through the trees. His breasts were smaller than Bill's but bigger than Lindsay's. Me dad farted again. Then burped.

"I don't feel so good, son."

He looked pale. He got up with difficulty and staggered upstairs. There was a crash and I ran up. My dad was standing in the bathroom and Bill was lying on his side.

"You nearly got it there, Frank," he said. "I felt something click."

Me dad stood there.

"I think I'm having an heart attack," he said. "I'm getting sharp pains in me chest. I think I'm a goner."

His suit matched the bathroom tiles.

"Loosen his clothing," said Bill from the floor, his mouth level with his feet.

Me mam came in, bringing the cigar smell with her.

"Dad's having an heart attack," I said.

She leaned over him and punched him in the face. I've never seen her so angry.

"You selfish bugger. You selfish bugger," she yelled and then dropped to her knees and began to weep.

We seemed to stay like that a long time. We must've looked like dummies in a shop window or something. My dad was breathing heavily, our Bill was trying to roll over onto his back, my mam was sobbing quietly and me ... well ... I was looking up at the ceiling and I was miles away. I was thinking about that little patch of garden we had at the new house. Now Lindsay wanted it for a vegetable patch but I fancied it for flowers. Chrysanths and such. It was a strange couple of minutes and I'll remember them all me life. It's always happened to me that, when I'm threatened or scared or excited. My mind goes into neutral and I just drift away. Look at me school reports it's all there: 'Richard is fond of dreaming', 'Richard often seems to be in a world of his own', 'Richard must get his head out of the clouds and his feet firmly planted on the ground.' It must only have been a minute or so really but then all sorts of things happened at once. Malcolm came rushing in, tripped over Bill and spilled the confetti over the bathroom. God knows why he'd opened the boxes. He said it was to save time at the church. Bill went into a kind of spasm, writhing on the floor like a seal. My dad, covered in confetti, suddenly smiled and said:

"Do you know? I feel a lot better."

And me mam reached over and pulled a great length of toilet roll and blew her nose on it spectacularly.

It was my wedding day. I was in the bathroom with a 23-stone man, a deputy head from Surrey and me mam and dad. We were all covered in confetti. At the other end of the village my wife-to-be was sitting in front of a mirror applying subtle make-up. Her mother, I knew, had lingering doubts about our family. Looking round the royal blue bathroom I knew I had no doubts at all.

# Reds Up, Sheffield Down

I can still remember the date, though I don't remember much about the day. I expect I did all the usual things: got up, went to work, maybe I was on playground duty. I remember the rain, because it stopped about half an hour before kick off. Tuesday May 4th 1982. I was 28 and had been waiting all my life for that night to arrive. The Reds needed just one point from the last game of the season, home to Grimsby, to clinch promotion, to the second division. For a supporter of a famous team, Arsenal or United, that probably wouldn't seem like something worth writing home about. But for us, it was a pinnacle not matched since we'd won the cup before the war. The First World War. We'd a new chairman at the time and in many ways he matched the club perfectly. He wasn't a wealthy man; in fact he had a stall on the market selling tights and what his sign coyly proclaimed to be, 'Ladies Foundation Garments'. He was christened Leonard Norton but was known throughout the town as 'Knickers Norton'.

In fact, that season he even had his own song. It usually came right after, 'C'mon you Reds' and 'They'll not be many going home', when a lone voice would strike up with the words, 'Oh knicker, knicker, knicker, knicker,

knicker Norton. Knicker, knicker, knicker, knicker, knicker Norton', and then the lads would start shouting, 'Off, off, off.' Lenny Norton had a saying though, that, looking back, probably summed everything up — the club, the team, the town and, maybe, us. It was in the programme one Saturday, in a very short column called 'The Chairman Speaks ...' In this, Lenny declared that he wouldn't rest until this club of ours had reclaimed its rightful place, the second division.

My dad had first taken me down to the ground when I was a lad. In fact he didn't pay for me until I was 10. The bloke on the turnstile that worked at me dad's pit would say, 'Reyt, squeeze through quick, before it clicks.' And then, fighting for breath, with my face buried in the front of my dad's gabardine, I'd stagger backwards through a narrow blackness to emerge in the cool air of the kop, where me dad would say, 'Y'alright Richard, love?' and, unable to speak, I'd just nod.

When I was 10, I think we were home to Workington, the inevitable finally happened. For some reason, we didn't beat the click and got stuck. Me dad went mad.

"What the bloody hell? Push will tha, push!"

Then the turnstile man said:

"It's clicked. Thi'll not get through now. Tha's stuck."

"I know I'm stuck. I'm not leet. Let us through, will tha?"

"Sorry pal, can't do nowt once it's clicked."

By now there was a big queue, which in itself was an event. The bloke at the front shouted through to us:

"Tha'll have to lift him."

"I'll bloody lift thee in a minute, if tha doesn't shut thi rattle."

We finally got into the ground, where my dad sat me down on the top step of the terrace and started to waft my sweating face with his cap.

"Y'alright, Richard?"

It was hard even to nod.

"Stand clear."

"Tha what?"

"Man down here. Make way, make way—stretcher."

It was Kenneth Bisby and his son, Harry. They were in the St John's and had their own dugout near the far corner flag, where they'd sit in full regalia through every home match. They lived near us and were big with the Primitive Methodists. My dad assured the disappointed Bisby that I was all right, and we trudged down to our usual perch near the front. We stood, freezing, as the Reds, after taking an early lead, slumped to another defeat.

Looking back, I think that's when my dad's faith started to ebb away. I don't know if it was the result or the knowledge that from now on he'd have to pay for me as well. But something died that day. As I got older, I could see the symptoms getting progressively worse. When I was 15 he stopped going, mid season, after a match against Brighton that we'd won 4–1. I couldn't understand it.

"Look, we're fifth now, two games in hand. If we keep

going like this, we'll get up into second and then it'll be first."

My dad just laughed. Then he leaned forward and using the same tone he adopted when outlining his conspiracy theory about the pit manager, the parson and Sir Stafford Cripps, said:

"Listen son, they'll never be in first and does tha know why they'll never be in first?"

"Why dad?"

"'Cos they don't want it. That's why. They might get into the second, I grant you that, but that'll be as far as it goes. Tha'll see. Its thi directors. Thi money men. They don't want first division wages. Why does tha think we always sells our best players?"

As the years went by he hardly ever went near the ground. I'd persuade him occasionally, usually around Christmas, but every time he showed up, they lost. Much to his delight. And as we walked back to the bus station, he'd smile a grim smile and say, 'What did I tell thee? They don't want it.'

So that night, May 4th, meant everything. We'd had a great year, never out the top six, quarter-finals of both cups and knocked out three first division teams on the way. As the season went by the crowd started to get bigger. The usual faithful 5,000 grew to six, seven, ten thousand. When spring came and we were still up there it became thirteen, fourteen, even fifteen thousand. Whole sections of the ground that I'd only ever known as empty concrete steps with the occasional bit of rosebay willow herb, started to fill with people. Men brought their sons, whole families turned up, women as well, much to me dad's disgust.

"Now what the hell does tha want women for at a match, eh?"

And my mother would smile and say:

"I think it's a good idea, letting women join in."

To which my dad would say, "Ahh, see what I mean. Road to nowhere, women" and stomp off to The Cross Keys.

I got to the ground an hour before the kick off, a previously unheard of necessity. Having endured the long winter campaign with the fog on the M62, snow at Carlisle and the pies at Rotherham, I wasn't going to lose my usual position on the East Terrace to some part timers who'd just turned up for the glory.

For some reason, it seemed vital to stand in exactly the same spot each week. It was towards the back, almost at the halfway line and exactly in line with the letter F on the advertising hoarding on the other side that read, 'Norton's: For Your Foundations'. There were three or four of us always stood there. We'd been at school together. We'd often have a pint after the match, just mates really and then there were the others. Familiar faces of men without names. We gave them names, being clever college lads and making our way in the teaching profession. There was 'Big Jock' who, strangely enough, was Scottish and six foot four. His thing was to arrive at one minute to three and stand right in front of a tiny old man we called, 'The Weasel'. Then there was 'Robbie Rattle'. He was, I suppose, a couple of steps short of a full terrace and, unusually even for our club, still owned and used a rattle. These had gone out in the 1960s. I had one for about three matches till me dad got fed up with it. He'd been on nights all week and I think it was the last straw when, celebrating a last minute equaliser, I whizzed my rattle round in front of his face. I can still remember him grabbing it from my hand and flinging it high into the floodlit night. It sailed over the back of the Kop and dropped into some nettles by the far wall. At full time I was all for scrambling down the back of the Kop to recover it but he wouldn't let me. Then, on the way home, as I fought back hot tears, he softened a bit and said, 'Gi o'er now, will tha? I'll get thee another. But dunt say nowt to thi mam.'

So there we were, May 4th 1982: me, the lads, Big Jock, The Weasel, Robbie Rattle and all the other faces — the man in the trilby that looked like Maigret, the fat kid from the building society and the three old men, who we called the wise monkeys, draped over the barrier next to us, visions in Harris tweed. Hundreds of faces. Thousands of faces. The whole town, 21,000 people packed onto the terraces. Old timers saying to each other, 'Aye, but it'll not last tha knows. Thi dunt want it.' First timers saying, 'Who's that at number nine?' And me, drinking it all in like the best pint of beer I'd had in my whole life.

Two things almost spoiled the evening. One was when

Grimsby, against the run of play and, in the opinion of 21,000 people, miles offside, took an early lead. There was an appalled silence as their players rolled about in front of our Kop, until one of the wise monkeys said quietly, 'Telled thee they didn't want it.' The moment when they scored was almost, but not quite, as bad as when the Reds had run out to a storm of applause that came rolling down the terraces in waves and suddenly turned to embarrassed laughter as we saw that the lads had been given some kind of special kit to wear for the big match. It had little white flashes on the shoulders that, from a distance, made them look like they were wearing brassieres.

It all came right in the second half. Two goals from the Reds, and then the worst 10 minutes of my life, as Grimsby pressed forward time after time. But that moment, when the referee finally blew for full time, was the best moment of my life. I'd never heard noise like it. Robbie Rattle's arm was just a blur, one of the wise monkeys flung his cap high into the night, and Big Jock turned round and lifted The Weasel off the ground. Old weasel protested, but only a bit, 'I've got angina, put me down.' And me, I was crying.

Later, I walked into the tap room to find me dad, who, true-to-form, had refused my invitation to the match.

"We've done it dad. Two – one. We're up. Promoted."

Usually he'd have gone into his 'It'll not last, they never wanted it' speech, but tonight was different. He looked at me, quietly, like he used to do when I was a little kid out of breath from the turnstiles, and said, 'I'm right glad for thi Richard, love. Right glad. But you sees Sheffield's gone down.'

"What you on about, dad? They weren't playing, were they."

"The HMS Sheffield. They've bloody sunk it."

"What?"

"Twenty one dead. Young lads, like thee."

And I didn't know what to say. Me and the old man had already clashed over the Falklands, like we did over most things by then. He was all for it. I had my usual wishy-washy doubts. I let him buy me a drink and we sat down together, neither of us speaking.

Later, after I'd dropped me dad off, I knew why I'd cried at the match. I'd cried for a picture in my head. Me, as a little boy, and my dad holding hands as we walked up the hill all those winters ago. And me, eight or nine years old, looking back through the steadily moving tide of coats and caps, gazing up at the big black sky and the red roof stand shining like a dream. But most of all, I'd been crying for me and me dad. We were never so close again as we were on those cold Saturdays when we'd won nothing, but anything was possible, so long as you believed.

# There's Always a Man
# in a Cardigan

Lindsay sat up and said:

"I've started."

I looked at the clock: '01:01'. It seemed more like a cry for help than a time.

"Are you sure?" I said, tentatively.

I remembered two days before when I'd come home from school to find her holding on to the occasional-table and trying to take her mind off things by watching Tony Hart make a mural out of sugar lumps. We'd dashed through Barnsley faster than the police did during the 'Ronald Biggs in Mexborough' rumour, but when we got to the maternity unit it was a false alarm.

"I'm sure," she said. "Get the car out, you're going to be a dad."

She came downstairs slowly, deliberately, her face occasionally twisting up with pain. I'd told her I was going to be there at the birth but now I wasn't so sure. I think really I'd have liked to pace about outside and then get called in to see a face in a shawl and start handing out cigars. For years, I didn't know that I'd been born. My mam said the nurse had brought me through the snow. I asked why the nurse had to bring me, and my mam said she would have brought me herself but she was in bed poorly at the time. Later, when I was at junior school, Pud Stennett explained how babies were born. It was a rainy Saturday afternoon in 1965 in my auntie's shed and me and Pud had just tried to smoke some balsa wood cigarettes.

"You know breasts?' he said.

Breasts. The word made me go red. He said it again:

"You know breasts?"

"Yes."

"Well you know the bits at the end?"

"What bits?"

"Nittles."

"Nittles?"

"Nittles. Women feed their babies through 'em. Well, that's how babies are born. Through the nittles."

"How do you mean?"

The balsa wood smoke was starting to get to me. I felt a bit sick. Pud lowered his voice as though my Auntie might be standing outside the shed, listening.

"Well half the baby's born through one nittle and the other half's born through the other nittle and then the doctor sews you together and that's why you've got a belly button. It's where your halves were put together by a doctor."

I was overwhelmed. I didn't know what to say. Then a sudden thought occurred to me:

"What about twins?" I asked.

Stennett's voice was even softer now.

"I know but I can't tell thi."

"I'll give thi all my spare civil war cards."

Pud Stennett loved civil war cards, and I saw he couldn't resist my offer. He leaned very close to me. His face looked old and wise in the stale balsa wood smoke.

"Four nittles," he said.

I got the car out of the garage and Lindsay struggled in. It was a clear, crisp moonless night in December, and I could see my breath as I closed the garage door. Funny thing about Pud Stennett. He ended up teaching biology.

The car started first time and we were off. Lindsay sat in the back, me driving slowly, trying not to panic. It was only a few months since I'd passed my test and I still wasn't too confident. Lindsay leaned forward and said:

"You can try second gear if you want," and I bit back with a stinging reply.

My Auntie Elsie always used to say, 'Tell 'em about the jam when the fire's gone out' which apparently meant 'Always try to keep people's mind off things.' So I said to Lindsay:

"Would you like some music on the 8-track? I've got Jethro Tull, Fairport Convention ..."

I was still into progressive in those days. She shook her head.

"Just try and drive a bit faster," she said.

I got up to 30 miles an hour and said:

"I'll tell you what. I bet we see an old bloke in a

cardigan walking a dog. I'll bet your first year's family allowance."

She didn't reply; she knew I was rambling.

It's been a theory of mine for years, that: The Old Bloke With The Cardigan and Dog Theory. It started when I was sixth-former and I used to go to the Corner Pin on a Friday night and get legless on two and a half pints of Barnsley Bitter. Me and my mates would stagger home after midnight and no matter what the weather was, we always saw a wizened old bloke in a cardigan walking a dog. We'd have competitions: who'd be first one to spot him? Would he be walking towards Barnsley up Kendray Hill or away from Barnsley towards Stairfoot? What colour would his cardigan be? Would it be buttoned? If so, how many buttons? And, the clincher: would he speak and if he spoke, what would he say? We had a points system: if he said 'Evening' or 'Goodnight', we got five points. If he was aggressive and said something like, 'Get on ooam before I crack yer' or 'You college lads shouldn't be drinking mucky beer', we got 10 points, but the crowning glory, if Barnsley FC had been playing that night, was if he said the immortal phrase, 'How's Barnsley gone on?' Thirty points. Magic!

We drove up the road, past the garden centre, through Ardsley and towards Barnsley. We still hadn't seen him and, funnily enough, I was really wanting to see him. While I was at college I'd worked the old man and the dog into a kind of folk-myth. He protected Barnsley, I'd say to open-gobbed lasses from the Home Counties; he's like the lamplighter, I'd say, the night watchman, the guardian angel of a dirty northern town. Then I'd turn slightly away and vomit spectacularly onto a pile of books that always contained *The Catcher in the Rye* and *The Great Gatsby*. The girls from the Home Counties would leave the room and I'd be alone with an engineer from Stockport called Miles. The rich are different from us.

We drove into the hospital grounds. I was going to park in the car park but Lindsay told me you were allowed to drive up to the door. At the door we were put in a lift, whisked to a ward, details were taken, efficient nurses bustled about, and I felt out of it. I'd got a joke ready. If they said, 'Do you want to be there at the birth?' I was going to say, 'Well, I was there at the conception so I may as well go for the double!' but nobody asked me.

A little nurse who looked like Roy Barraclough took Lindsay off to a room.

"I'd like to be there," I said, quietly.

"We'll call you when we're ready, Mr Matthewman," said Roy.

I walked over to the window. Barnsley was laid out, orange and black under the stars. I tried to recognise individual streets and imagined blokes with dogs and cardigans on each one. I became suddenly, unaccountably, worried. My mate Trev at school, he's got three, and he told me I'd suffer from The Sudden Worry. 'Just before it's born, Richard, you'll be sure that it'll come out with three heads and more legs than a hockey team but you'll convince yourself that you'll still love it.' I hadn't believed it before, but now I could feel it creeping over me. After a while a nurse came and said:

"You can go and see your wife now, Mr, er, Matthewman."

She led me into a little room. Lindsay was dressed in a sort of smock, sitting on the bed. There was a portable telly in one corner and a couple of paperback books on a shelf.

"They say it'll be a while yet. It could be morning before anything happens," she said.

I wandered over to the telly and switched it on. *Son of Godzilla*. A dinosaur was just hatching out of an egg. Scientists watched, their lips mouthing furious Japanese, but sounding American. The dinosaur wobbled out of the bits of eggshell and stood unsteadily. I turned it off. The Sudden Worry returned. When ours was born it would look like a triceratops.

The room, like all hospital rooms, was red hot. It reminded me of afternoons in my grandad's greenhouse, listening to his chest rattling like waves over shingle. I was sweating. In the rush to get dressed I'd just pulled a sweater on with nothing underneath, so I couldn't even take it off. I said to Lindsay:

"Are you okay if I just pop outside for a minute, get some fresh air?"

She waved me away. Being there at the birth was for my benefit, not hers. I noticed a door marked 'Waiting Room', and pushed it open slowly. It was pitch dark. I felt along the wall for the light switch and turned it on. There was a mass cry of 'GEEOR!' and I came face to face with half a dozen Barnsley dads-to-be who had been trying to sleep on the chairs, the tables, and in one case, the floor. They all sat, stunned in the harsh light, trying to rub their faces off the front of their heads. One man, although he was fully dressed, was casting about for his clothes and mumbling:

"Ah didn't think ah were on days this week. Ah didn't think I were on days."

A big man with an NCB jacket on said:

"What is it, doctor? A lad or a lass. If it's a lad she'll kill me. She reckons Friday nights makes lads."

I went out. Not everybody wanted to be present at the birth. I went down in the lift and walked out into the freezing air. The sweat dried on my brow and I began to shiver. I was nervous. More than that, I was terrified. My old life was going to end, here, tonight, December 9th 1981, and a new life was going to begin with responsibilities and nappies and sleepless nights and a baby that looked like a triceratops. I had to be calm, had to be strong, for Lindsay's sake.

Then I identified the source of my worry, admitted it, faced up to it: I hadn't seen the bloke with the cardigan and the dog. Daft as it seemed, I needed to see him, needed something to link the old life to the new life in the freezing December air.

I walked through the car park to the hospital entrance. I looked up and down the road, quickly. Nobody. A black taxi zoomed past with an old lady sitting in the back clutching a handbag. Overhead, an aeroplane rumbled through the clear sky, its lights flashing. I needed to go back to Lindsay, but I needed to see the bloke with the dog. It was like when I was little and I had to do things in a certain order on Saturday night: first, have my bath and hair wash, then sit downstairs on the settee with my jamas and dressing gown on watching Richard Basehart in *Voyage to the Bottom of the Sea*, eating a bag of plain crisps and keeping as many of them in my mouth as I could before I swallowed any.

Suddenly, just as I was about to give up and go back into the steaming hospital, I saw him; the man with the dog and the cardigan. I couldn't believe it. I walked down the road towards him, to make sure he was real. His little Jack Russell barked at me. He looked at me like I was mad, or drunk, or both.

"Evening," he said.

And I recognised him! It was Flour-on-Hands! He used to work at the tennis-ball factory and delighted in telling us students about all the times during the day he and his wife made love.

"I once came up behind her while she were baking scones," he said. "And we did it there and then over the sink, and she still had flour on her hands!"

We christened him Flour-on-Hands after that, although we never called him that to his face, and seeing him now, this night of all nights, linked all my past and my future together in a way I couldn't fathom.

"Flour-on-Hands!" I said.

I couldn't remember his real name.

"What the hell are you on about?" he said.

The Jack Russell was growling now.

"Richard Matthewman, tennis-ball factory, 1975," I said. "My wife's having a baby in there."

As I pointed to the hospital lit up like a great ocean liner, I realised that's where I should be, with my future, not my past, and I ran across the car park like my shoes were on fire.

They were taking Lindsay into the delivery suite when I dashed out of the lift.

"Where've you been?" she shouted.

"It's okay, I've seen the man with the cardigan and the dog," I said.

But I knew she wasn't listening. I followed her into the room where new life began.

# The Enemy Within

I was slumped in the armchair and the *Channel 4 News* was about to start. It had been a terrible day at school, what with the kids playing pickets and coppers in the playground, and half of them not able to go on the school trip to Scarborough to round off our term's topic on the sea because their dads were on strike and they couldn't afford it.

Then to cap it all, Uncle Albert had tried to phone me at school. Luckily I'd been on the field with first year so they couldn't get to me but the message was: 'Phone him urgent.'

Uncle Albert and his bloody banjo. He'd been serenading them on the picket lines, as a balmy spring rolled into a wonderful summer. Mainly country and western favourites with the odd popular hymn and one or two compositions of his own. These he called his 'little Alberts' and he was up to little Albert 438 at the last count. In the end, the Metropolitan Police and the more solvent pickets got a collection together to get rid of him. He thought he was doing his bit for 'industrial relations' and in a way he was. He'd been round 16 pits so far in South and West Yorkshire and there were rumours he'd have to move to the North East soon.

He gave all the money to the strike, or he said he did, but I'd noticed him strutting around town in a new blazer last week.

The phone rang, ten past seven. I knew it had to be Uncle Albert. I could even tell before he spoke by the way he drew a long breath to shout with. He'd never fathomed the telephone.

"Richard lad, I need your help."

"How d'you mean?"

"I have a benefit tonight at bottom club."

I knew what was coming and I didn't want it. I really didn't want it.

"And me car's in garage and I wondered if you could give me a lift? It's for the cause. Just me and the banjo and the cassettes."

The cassettes, 600 of them, give or take a dozen. A Banjo Night with Albert 'Banjo' Wright. It was a bloody heavy box. They weren't selling that well. Hard times. Still, there was no way out of it. I was obliged. Morally obliged. I drove round to his place. The box was big and heavy and there was no lid. Uncle Albert's face looked out at me dozens of times, grinning.

"Right then, lad," said Uncle Albert.

"Do I look okay, then? Wyatt Earp, eh?"

He was all in black. Black hat, black shirt, black string tie, black belt, black trousers and jet black boots. His eyes gleamed and I could tell he was going to tell me a joke. Uncle Albert's jokes were as bad as his banjo playing.

"This Red Indian goes t'dentist because his teeth are in

a terrible state. All chipped and cracked and falling out and the dentist takes one look inside his mouth and says, 'You've been biting too much dust,'."

Uncle Albert. There was a time when every family in this village seemed to have an Uncle Albert — a bit eccentric, out of the ordinary, soft as a brush, what your media people would call a 'character'. There was our Uncle Albert: banjo and jokes, Mrs Copeland: violins and funerals, Annie Griffiths: beard and shouting, and that Welsh bloke with the extra thumb and munching Mick. It was when charity first came back into fashion. Mick McNulty, he'd eat anything for charity or 'them crippled biddies' as he used to call them. He started off in a small way, custard on his Yorkshires, Sunday afternoons in the top club. Then it was fish fingers and jelly at the chapel fête. Then it went to his head, think he got a bit carried away, never out of the Chronicle. He ate four dozen pickled eggs. He drank a jug of frogspawn larded with sherry and then finished up eating a Honda 90 on the Cross Keys car park, bank holiday Monday. Munching Mick, he's dead now. Choked on a haddock bone in Chapel St Leonards. Dead on arrival. They all thought it was a stunt.

The bottom club was packed. Loads of miners there and their mates and families. Lots of parents from the school. Some I always saw at parents evening, some I wouldn't have recognised if I hadn't had them pointed out to me. It was rumoured, as it always was, that Arthur Scargill was going to turn up. So a lot of the curious and faithful had grabbed front row seats. Uncle Albert was going on first, followed by the local hand bell team, recently renamed Edderthorpe Hand Bells Against Pit Closures and then an alternative comedy duo from the South called George and his Friend the Staple Gun. Oh, and there was Edna, the poetess.

There were three consistent things about those benefit nights in the spring and summer of 1984. One was that somebody would sing *The Laughing Policeman* in a sinister way and think they were the first to think of it. One was that Arthur were going to be there (and sometimes he was and sometimes he wasn't) and the third was that Edna the poetess would be there reading her terrible poems. To be honest, I was the only one who found them terrible. To me they were over sentimentalised, technically inept hymns to a working class that never existed.

The concert room was long and low with windows all down one side and a long bar doing less than brisk business down the other. The only person at the bar as I sat down was Johnny Cameron, leader of the hand bell ringers and an alcoholic since infant school as far as anyone could tell. He taught Geography, erratically, at the comp and was very big in the union. I'd done a bit for the NUT for a while and I was always surprised how passionate and articulate he was at union meetings. He reckoned the whiskey kept his brain supple. He had that scrawniness that some drinkers have and that night he was wearing a white t-shirt with "NUT NUM" the words crossing at the 'U'. He tried to flog us all some at a meeting and although he'd sold a few, he was the only one who had so far dared go out in one. The lights dimmed and the concert secretary Donald McKiver came on stage, wearing a suit it was rumoured he bought for the coronation.

"Good evening. Tonight, another excellent night of entertainment to show sodilarity…"

He always said, 'sodilarity'. I thought it was a joke, at first. It wasn't.

"… sodilarity with the striking miners of this village to whom all monies raised will accrue."

The room cheered and a ragged chorus of 'Here we go, here we go, here we …' was allowed to run its course. Donald raised his hands for silence and said:

"So straight on with the entertainment and who better to start with than your very own, your own, Albert 'Banjo' Wright."

Albert got no applause. Everyone talked all the way through the banjo playing and they even talked through his joke about the Red Indian biting dust. It wasn't that Uncle Albert played badly; he just played mechanically, woodenly, like a child persistently knocking at a door. After 20 minutes he went off to no applause and the hand bell ringers came on. They got some applause, mainly due to the fact that at least three quarters of them were lower sixth form girls.

I stood at the bar with a half. Of course it was good to see people fighting for what they believed in. Of course it was good to see people using entertainment and laughter to fight off despair, but I just felt empty. I felt nothing.

Edna the poetess got up. There was a reverence as if we were in a well-lit church. Her poems were getting worse, it seemed to me, but who was I to judge? She was a short, stubby woman, of indeterminate age, who had been writing poems for years on all kinds of topics and sometimes having them published in *The Barnsley Chronicle*. The pit strike and the benefit concerts had been a Godsend to her. Night after night of willing audiences all over South Yorkshire. She finished one poem to rapturous applause and launched into another.

> 'The men who stand on picket line,
> Might land in jail or at least a fine.
> While her, who sits at number 10,
> Plays with the future of striking men.
> Who only want to stop the pits closing,
> And England to stop her dozing.'

The poem went on. I wandered over to Uncle Albert to persuade him to go home. I'd got a busy day the next day, trying to drag up funds from somewhere to make sure the whole lot of them could go on the Scarborough trip.

"Can't we just stay a bit longer, lad?" he whined. "There's supposed to be a Channel Four producer here tonight to look at the double act from London and they reckon they might be taking new acts on for a show about the miners' benefits."

I looked around the room. None of the people in it looked remotely like a Channel 4 producer or, on the other hand, they all did. We'd had one or two in school during the strike. I said I didn't mind what they filmed as long as I got a few quid out of it for the school funds. One of them called me a Thatcherite as he pressed twenty quid into my palm. And maybe I wasn't as insulted as I should've been.

Uncle Albert went on patrol, passing between the tables, looking at people. I caught his eye as he stood behind a table of what I knew to be tutors from the local FE College. He raised his thumb and held four triumphant fingers in the air. The room was strangely quiet now. There was a sense of anticipation. Maybe Scargill really was going to come. McKiver got up. He looked oddly nervous.

"And now a little treat. Something a bit different. Two lads who are making a bit of a name for themselves on the alternative circuit."

He read 'alternative circuit' from a piece of paper; it sounded as though he believed it was part of a wiring diagram.

"Please welcome: Eddy and his Friend the Staple Gun."

There was no applause. There was a shocked silence. A young, slim man walked on. He was completely naked, except for a red g-string. Behind him another man was dressed as Hitler. The slim man looked round and he grabbed the mic.

"This is a bit of a dump," he said and there was one embarrassed laugh from a lower sixth form girl.

The Hitler look-alike goose-stepped forward. I

remembered something I'd seen in the *Guardian* about these two. They were the very edge of avant-garde comedy. Insulting audiences until they succumbed to laughter or embarrassment or both. This was going to be interesting. Hitler pointed to Edna the poetess. He did more than point at her. He climbed off the stage and jabbed his gauntleted finger straight at her lumpy breasts in the crimpelene jumper she always wore.

"Is this what they call a close knit community around here?"

The silence grew. And lengthened. And widened. A pint pot hurtled through the air, gleaming in the harsh stage lights. The room was turning ugly. I looked round for Uncle Albert but he'd gone. I left the room and drove home.

I'd been home for about half an hour when the doorbell went. It was Uncle Albert. He was breathless and his clothes dirty. He pushed past me and slumped onto the settee.

"Lock the door," he said.

He was holding the neck of his banjo. Just the neck.

"What the hell's wrong?" I asked.

"I went down t'picket line, I couldn't stand it in the club. Those blokes got on me wick. There was a bit of pushing and shoving. A rumour that somebody might be going back to work. Then all hell broke loose. Coppers rushing about, blokes shouting, God knows what about. Thank Christ I left me cassettes in the club. Some bugger trod on me banjo and I gave a copper a good crack with this bit."

He held up the neck. Uncle Albert, the warrior.

"What's happening to the world, kid?" he asked.

I couldn't answer. I thought about Edna the poetess, her terrible poems and the way that lad dressed as Hitler had insulted her. It was grotesque. A dream. I told one of the brighter kids at school that we were living through history, but I didn't even believe that anymore. Uncle Albert and I sat in silence. There was a hammering on the door. I got up. Uncle Albert got up too.

"Tell 'em I'm not here, kid," he said.

I bet it's a Channel 4 producer, I thought. I opened the door. A huge copper stood there. He had his helmet off.

"Where is he? The maniac with the banjo."

"Are you from Channel Four?" I said.

He didn't get it. He looked at me closely.

"I know you," he said. "It's Richard Matthewman, int it, the clever kid?"

It was Henry Ford, my best mate from school. I hadn't seen him for years. I stood and looked at him. I was clever. He was clever. I went to grammar school. He didn't. It was 1984. I was sheltering a dangerous banjo player, Uncle Albert, the enemy within. I looked straight at him.

"I don't know what you're talking about," I said and closed the door.

# Going South

I'm surrounded by boxes. There's no carpet on the floor. No curtains at the window. An orange streetlight is splashed across the chimney breast. Across the road, Gerry and Margaret have gone to bed. Someone's taking a bath at the Reynolds' house and Frank Johnson is walking the dog he bought when his wife died. And I'm sitting on a box and it's 00:41 in green numbers and the radio is playing *Sailing By* and I'm singing along with it. I'm 38 years old, a grown man, allegedly, and here I am, putting words to *Sailing By*.

To tell you the truth, I'm drunk. Well, a bit drunk. Put it this way, I've gone beyond the sense of well being, through merriment and all encompassing bonhomie and come to rest in a place called 'dazed reflection'. Which is a couple of stages short of dancing in the taproom or falling down a hole in the road on the way home. Which, incidentally, I managed to do at our Anthony's stag night. There were three of us: me, our Anthony and Nigel Fleet. But why he should've been there I can't remember. He's a supermarket manager in Kidderminster now. We took a shortcut through the new buildings. Someone had moved the warning signs, and down we went. Three new suits, one bag of chips, a full pint glass of beer and half a bottle of vodka all wrecked at one go. Not to mention our Anthony's prospects. People still comment on how unusual it is to have wedding photographs that don't actually feature the groom. But if you look carefully at that big group, both families, friends of the bride and groom and anybody else who wants to be on, you can just see a chap on the extreme right wearing sunglasses, that's our Anthony.

Last time I felt like this was after me dad's funeral. Eleven o'clock at the house, then church, crem, and afterwards the community centre. Slippy ham on green plates. Bustling women with their coats off but their hats on, ministering tea and wise words about the follies of old men, everywhere, since time began. I ended up, as you do, in a corner with a strange little mixed group and a bottle of whiskey. There was me — the bereft son —, my cousin Mike, who I hadn't recognised earlier at the crem due to his incredible weight gain since marriage and furniture retailing had removed him to Worksop. There was Billy Hides who worked at the pit with me dad and a woman called Marjorie, who remained silent throughout apart from the one phrase, 'Well, he loved his cricket, I'll say that.' Which she would toss in at apparently random intervals. Oh yes, and there was my Auntie Eileen from Mexborough, who was 86 and had been the one to produce the whiskey from inside her handbag.

We got very reflective that afternoon. Reflective and confidential. Billy Hides told us that he'd once had a trial with Arsenal, which I didn't find too hard to believe given how boring he is. Our Michael leaned over at one point and in the loudest stage whisper I've ever heard told us all that Worksop was 'a hell of a place, after dark.' We all nodded, expecting more, but he just slumped back into his chins. Then Marjorie said, 'They play cricket in Worksop, don't they?' Later, I almost overstepped the mark by revealing the pathetic details of my one encounter with illegal substances when a student. Chewed between two slices of bread. There was no discernable mood enhancement. Then, about four in the afternoon, old Eileen started telling us about her part in the Spanish Civil War. Billy sent out for more whiskey and then we all got way beyond day's reflection and ended up singing *The Red Flag* in perfect harmony, as Gladys Lenton mournfully swept the floor around us and her husband Joseph stacked chairs and wondered what life without Gladys might have been like.

But tonight, I'm just reflective. My last night in this house. This street. This village. My last night in this life. Tomorrow I'll load the last of these boxes onto a self-drive hire van and away down the M1. Wife and kids, new job, new life all waiting. Start Monday and do you know, apart from three years at university, I've spent all my life here. This house and two other houses, all within half a mile of each other and now I'm off ... south.

It's been a strange day. I got the van this morning. Then straight up the motorway. Got here about two o'clock. Finished the last of the packing up in here. Strange place, empty houses, bigger suddenly, bare, neat. Then about four o'clock I had this idea I'd fix that dripping tap. The cold tap on the washbasin in the bathroom. I mean Lindsay's been at me for years to do something about it. First thing she said to me when she came back after our trial separation during the strike, 'Fix that tap'. Stupid really, I know, but well, I thought it would pass the time, give me something to do. I think I must have been in a daze. The motorway, the empty house, the silence, but it was only as I unscrewed the top of the tap that it dawned on me that I'd never changed a washer in my life. It was in my head that dads change washers on taps, like they made the fire first thing in a morning or did the veg on Sundays. I must've been thinking about me dad I suppose, he did things like that. All these thoughts were going through me head just at the moment a jet of cold water suddenly fountained between my fingers and sprayed up the mirror. It was then I remembered a wet Saturday afternoon with me dad when I was about 10, both of our heads is in his cap, crammed under me mam's sink unit.

"Tha sees, Richard, afore tha does owt with water, orlus, I mean orlus switch it off at the mains. It's the same with the electric, 'cos if thi dunt, thi'll be in a right tackin."

Wise words dad, because a 'right tackin' is not a good thing to be in as I was rapidly finding out now. First, I tried to screw the tap back together. It wouldn't go. In fact, it seemed to fall into more bits than I realised it had. Also me hand felt like a piece of raw haddock. Next, I groped with my left hand for a towel. I found the towel rail and then realised that all the towels were 150 miles down the M1. By now, panic was setting in. I had a vision of a pool, a pond, a lake, a waterfall down the stairs, having to swim out into the street, getting the bends, police divers, the house collapsing into a worthless lagoon, divorce, the sack.

For almost a minute I tried to bale out the water between cupped hands into the bath. Then I heard me dad's voice. 'Orlus, and I mean orlus, switch it off at the mains. 'Cos watter will orlus find a way.'

I ran downstairs, as best a man can run in saturated corduroy trousers and, skidding across the kitchen tiles, managed to find the stop tap under the sink and with the last of my fast ebbing strength, turned it off. Then I sat there, soaked on the floor and I started laughing. In the past when people in films had done that in moments of crisis I'd always found it hard to believe. A bit over-done, overdramatic, put on. Or as me mam would've said 'effected'. But not now. It was at that precise moment that Bill Houghton from next door tapped on the window. Through me tears I could just make out his features, the horn rims, the trilby with a feather, the tie and the cardigan, his mouth moving like a fish. Eventually I managed to get to me feet and, finding the kitchen door locked and the key's whereabouts a complete mystery, I yelled out those wonderful words of childhood:

"You'll have to come to the other door."

Then louder:

"I say, you'll have to come to the front. The other door."

He did so.

"Richard. Alright, lad?"

"Fine Bill, fine."

"Only I heard noises and that. I thought house were empty and, well, missus loves *Crimewatch*, thi knows."

"Very kind, Bill. Very neighbourly."

"Only tha can't be too carefully, can tha? I mean, these days."

Bill, since his early retirement from the Home Coal Offices, had been firmly of the opinion that civilisation was well into the back straight of the last lap and that to venture beyond the top of the street would lead to the inevitable sacking and looting of what he'd always called 'his property'. Fuelled by tabloid headlines and a constant scanning of all the TV and radio news bulletins, he'd come to believe that the only hope lay in himself and his wife operating a rota, rather like the Naval watch system, a sort of four hours on, four hours off and never go out at the same time, except in an emergency, in which case leave all the lights on plus the telly and Radio 2.

"Any road," Bill continued. "What were tha doing on floor? I thought tha'd had a stroke at first, laid there twitching. That's how it took Nora Brown, tha knows. Then I thought, 'No, he's only a young fella, it'll be a mugging.' Does tha know, Richard, they said on't radio yesterday that they'd mugged old ladies in an old people's 'ome. Does thi know what they took? Does thi? Nine bloody pence."

As Bill said this, his voice rose to a crescendo of triumph. All his opinions, his and his missus' world view, completely vindicated.

"No I'm fine really. Bit of accident with the plumbing."

"Tha wants to get to Dr Galvin with that."

"Oh yes," I laughed, weakly.

I managed to get rid of Bill after about half an hour.

"Yeah, going tomorrow. Yeah, for good. Well, quite a wrench, yeah. All these years, born and bred, good job though, oh yes. A step up. Yeah, me dad would've been pleased."

Then he fixed the tap for me like men of his generation can. As he was leaving, he turned to me and, pushing back his trilby, said:

"Tha sees, Richard. I know tha a clever bloke and that but tha must always turn the watter off at the mains first, 'cos the watter is like a crime, it'll orlus find a way. Any road, I best get back. She's been in there on her own for the best part of an hour and ..."

He glanced meaningfully toward the top of the street, so I cleared up, mopped up, dried out and then at about half seven had a walk to the cricket club for a couple of steady pints. Well, more like half a dozen really.

Funny place, the cricket club. It's more like a big wooden shed with a red tin roof and a lot of do-it-yourself upholstery. Most of the clientele wouldn't know the difference between long leg and a leg of lamb, but go in for the twin attractions of cheap beer and surliness. The former provided by a sponsorship deal with the local brewery, the latter by Harry Hammerton, steward, spin bowler and full time surl.

"Evening, Harry," I said.

"What the hell do you want?"

"Pint, please."

"Pint? Do they have them where thi going?"

I smiled.

"I thought it were pink gins and champagne outta shoes, that kind of carry on."

"A pint will be fine, ta."

"I thought tha'd gone, left, school mastering down south, pulling ladder up behind."

"Tomorrow, Harry."

"Ah well. That's last we'll see of thi then. Mind you it's finished this place, int it?"

"Well I wouldn't ..."

"Oh aye. Finished, done out. They've all spent their lump sums. All them new Nissans and Sierras starting to rust a bit. All that double-glazing starting to steam up. All them grandkids in prams starting school. Nah, it's done. Just litter, crime and rudeness now."

That were rich coming from him.

I sat down in the corner near the window. Behind me it was getting dark. Bill Slater was moving the wicket for the Sunday afternoon match. Some kids were playing on the field with an old bat and a tennis ball. We used to play cricket, on the beach at Brid. Me, me mam and dad, our Shirley, me Uncle Albert with his banjo, my Auntie Nancy with her knitting and her Alan and Phillip that went to Australia. Cricket at Bridlington. Took it seriously. Two sets of stumps, a spongy, last man batting on, six and out into the sea and real bails. My best score was 39 not out before bad light stopped play. We'd get back to the lodge for our dinner. Full board, three massive fried meals, getting weighed on them big red scales on the prom first Saturday night and then again before we went home to see if we'd put any weight on and we always had. One year our Alan had put three stone on. It were mainly pennies from the slots and half a dozen back numbers of Parade off the Tuesday market. He's got a bungalow near Brisbane now, our Alan. My Uncle Albert still sends him the Parade, I think. The 1960s; smiles and sunshine. Whole streets shipped east for a week and you'd always see somebody you knew on the first afternoon while you were waiting to get into the lodge.

It's all gone now. Barnsley feast week, Bridlington, proper cricket with bails, three spongy meals a day and a Parade down your vest.

I turned round and watched old Bill Slater marking the creases for tomorrow's match. Behind him the wind was blowing autumn through the trees over on the far side and, beyond that, a pleasant curved, green view where the puts used to be. It could've been anywhere. Or nowhere. It certainly didn't feel like home anymore.

# The Outsider

I went up to see me mother last weekend. I only stayed one night. We'd a parent-teacher do on the Saturday so, obviously, being deputy head, I had to be back for that. They're dreadful dos but it's expected. Anyway, my mother had phoned me on the Thursday evening, which came as a surprise as she isn't on the phone. Me and Lindsay have been on at her ever since my dad died to get a phone but she always refuses. Then when we moved down south I said that I'd pay for a phone putting in so we could ring her every week, but she wouldn't hear of it.

She was phoning from Nelly Swift's, who lives three doors down. I was at school with their Eric. He's a doctor now who lives in Wales. We'd just settled down with a bottle of Beaujolais and some dips when the phone rang and as I reached across to answer it, I knocked the bottle over with what hurdlers call my trailing leg. Then spinning round to try and catch it, I put my foot into the tarasamalata. So naturally, when I picked the phone up, I was a bit tetchy. It wasn't just the mess — we keep getting calls for a taxi firm and we'd already had four that evening. What with that and the national curriculum, I'm afraid I shouted.

"Hello?"

It was a woman's voice.

"Look, this is not A1 Taxis, for the last time."

"It's Richard, int it? Only your mother would like a word."

Then it clicked.

"Oh, Mrs Swift. Sorry about that. Is something wrong?"

I could hear her passing the phone across to me mother saying, 'He's there now, love. But I think he's a bit canned up.'

By now, I'd somehow managed to put a thin pink streak of tarasamalata halfway up the wall.

"Richard?"

"Mother, what's wrong?"

"Have you been drinking?"

"What? Mother! I'm nearly 41, what's wrong?"

"Oh. Nowt really."

I heard Nelly prompting her:

"Tell him. He'll soon sober up when you tell him. Our Eric's the same. They're always having that there dinner wine, and he's a doctor."

"Mother, what's going on?"

"Well I've had a bit of trouble, love. I don't like bothering you but ..."

"What sort of trouble?"

She'd had a break in. That afternoon when she'd been at the over-60s. They hadn't taken much; she hasn't got much to take but they'd made a mess of the house.

"I'll come up mother."

"You will not."

"I will. I'll come up tomorrow after work. Make sure you're all right, help you get straight."

"I don't want any fuss."

I suppose it's about 140 miles, and it's strange but every time I go back it seems further than the last time. It was eight o'clock by the time I got there. I'm not sure what I was expecting after her phone call but the house seemed to be as immaculate as ever. Coal fire blazing, polished brasses round the fireplace and the fruit bowl with two apples and an orange in it and, of course, all the photographs. Quite a lot were of me. There was me as a baby, me in grammar school uniform, and then me, in what my mother always insists on calling, 'Cap and Gown' on the day I graduated. (What a terrible day, that was. I didn't realise until it was too late how uncool it was to actually turn up in person to collect your degree. Most of my friends went straight to the beaches of Greece or to summer camps in America or even, in one case, a job. Instead I had to meet my mother and dad at Leicester Station and then endure what the ticket called, 'A Sherry Reception'. When it came to getting my degree, they got my name wrong: 'B.A. Honours, Richards, Matthews.' And I trooped across the stage to where a lesser member of the Royal Family shook my hand and said, 'Well Done, Mr Matthews.' Up on the balcony, my mother, prepared to accept even a change of name as long as there was a cap and gown in it for me, applauded long and loud.)

As I had expected, my mam had cooked a massive

meal. Roast beef, Yorkshire puddings, three veg, gravy. She'd cooked it just for me and wouldn't have anything herself. So I sat in the living room with a meal that would've kept a family of four going for a week, while she did things in the kitchen. We had a conversation; well she did most of the talking.

"It's not so much what they took; you know I've nowt worth taking. No, it's the fact that they've been in, in my house, that somebody, a stranger, has been in ... going through my things ... I don't know how to put it. It's not nice, Richard."

'Nice' and 'very nice' were my mother's favourite superlatives as in, 'Those trousers are nice, love' or 'Our Richard and Lindsay have got a very nice bungalow, you know.' In my mother's hands the word 'nice' took on a great subtlety, like the time when, newly back from college, I'd gone out and bought a jacket made from two different types of denim. And she'd looked at me and said, 'Yes Richard, it's quite nice.' Which really meant, 'All that education and he turns up wearing a jacket made from two types of denim. Where did me and his dad go wrong?'

"So what did they actually take, mam?"

"Oh, just a few bits and pieces."

"Like what?"

"Nothing valuable. Do you want another Yorkshire pudding? I can soon do you one."

She came back into the room wiping her wet hands on her pinny, like she'd been doing all my life, and most of hers.

"Well, if you must know, they took your dad's watch."

"His pit watch?"

"Yes."

"Bastards."

"Richard! Language. You know I don't like language in this house, and your dad didn't either."

Even though I felt like crying, I smiled, remembering a day when I was 14 and Eric Swift and me had been in the front room playing Subbuteo; we'd a league at the time. I was 'Edward Street United' and he were 'Swift Celtic'. Anyway, Eric missed an open goal and said, 'Hell Fire' and I said, 'Tha're a dozy get, thee Swifty' and at that moment me dad walked in and shouted at us. 'Talk right will ye, grammar school lads, theeing and tharing all along. Talk reyt and stop swearing.'

"I wish they hadn't taken his pit watch, Richard. All them years he took that to work and then when he's gone ..."

And suddenly my mother's face crumpled and the tears came. I held her, just for a minute, and then she pulled away, wiping her eyes on the back of her pinny, sniffed and said:

"I'll mash some more tea."

I just sat there chewing a piece of meat, over and over again, and thinking of my dad winding his watch up, pulling on his cap and striding out into the dark for another shift. He'd always shout to my mother in the other room, 'Right, I'm off' and she'd shout back, 'Aye, lock the door will you?' and then he'd be gone.

I stayed in my old room that night in a narrow bed. I

was tired but couldn't sleep. An owl hooted, it sounded very close. I went to the window and looked out and there it was, about 10 feet away, perched on the lamppost. It turned its head like owls do, gave me a long, hard look and launched itself softly into the night. Then I realised how quiet it was. When I was a kid it was so noisy at night. Traffic, lorries, trains shunting coal wagons down to Wath, and a sort of background humming. It never kept me awake, not like silence and owls. It was a comfortable noise saying, 'Your dad's at work and you and your mam are safe and things will get better for ever and ever.'

Next morning, Saturday, I took my mother shopping into town. It was raining. Even though I'd been away for less than two years the place seemed to have changed. Shops that had been there since God was a lad were gone, replaced by tat with signs saying, 'Everything One Pound' or 'Liquidation Sale: Everything Must Go.' We walked through the market; at least that seemed the same. Mam bought some fruit.

"Mother? Who do you buy that fruit for?"

"You what?"

"That fruit? Who do you buy it for? You don't eat fruit!"

"Well you like it, Richard."

"But I'll be going back tonight."

"Aye well, it'll do if anybody calls."

"We'll have a bit of lunch, shall we mam?"

"Lunch?"

"You know, dinner, in a pub. We could go to The Keys if you like?"

"We could not."

"Why? It'd be nice to see Eddie and Marion again."

"They've gone."

"Never?"

"Couldn't make it pay. Brewery put a manager in and they've altered it all. They only let young 'uns go in, now. It's all loud music and flashing lights."

So we drove on a bit and ended up at a place that I used to go with Lindsay when we were courting, The Mason's Arms. It looked newly refurbished, but me mother seemed dubious.

"They've changed this place an' all."

"Well it looks all right to me."

But I was wrong. The Mason's had become part of a national chain and had changed beyond all recognition. It used to be kept by a man of legendary rudeness called Willis Fletcher. People used to travel miles just in the hope of being insulted by him or, better still, witness it happen to someone else. I remember once when a bloke came in and said, 'Excuse me landlord, can you tell me the way to Doncaster?' And old Willis, without looking up from his book, had said, 'I certainly cannot, good day to you and shut the door on the way out.' But Willis Fletcher was long gone, replaced it seemed by a team of young children in waistcoats saying things like, 'Smoking or non smoking?' and calling me 'Sir'. There were signs and notices everywhere. There was even a list of instructions for getting served. First, find your table, note table number, order your food at the food counter. The food was ordinary beyond belief and one of the waist-coated children even said the words, 'Chef's preparing your meal now, sir', just as the microwave in the kitchen went 'ping'.

So we sat there, me and my mother, both of us pretending to enjoy the food, with her knowing she could have cooked something twice as good in half the time, and me wishing I'd let her.

"Everything all right, sir, madam?"

"Lovely, thanks."

The boy smiled as he'd been trained to smile and sailed on to where an extremely old couple were sitting with an even older woman, who was saying the words, 'I shall try to get him out next week though, if I can get his legs going.'

Afterwards we went for a drive over the common, nearly as far as the A1. On the way back I turned down the pit lane where me dad used to work. The lane only ever went to the pit and now it went nowhere. Just concrete, bricks, rubbish and black land shining in the wet. At the end of the lane was a very old caravan. In front of it, sitting on hardback kitchen chairs, were two fat women in pink housecoats, drinking mugs of tea. As I turned the car round one of the women waved and my mother waved back.

"That's Betty Humphreys off top street and that's their Ida with her. They're holding a vigil. Reckoned to be stopping there till government re-opens pit."

"But there's nowt left of the pit, mam."

She didn't seem to hear me.

"Aye, they've had all sorts down here, you know. Council men, MPs, Africans, they've even had *News at Ten*."

"It's too late now though, int it?"

"Too late for this place. God knows what your dad would've thought."

Some families might have talked, held each other, cried. We just went quiet as the car wipers squeaked on the glass.

"I wish I'd still got his watch, Richard."

"I know mam, I know."

Pulling away, I looked back in the mirror and saw one of the pit women holding a radio high above her head and turning it slowly as though she was trying to catch a message from somewhere far away.

# Where The Cage Was

I walked over to the wardrobe and hung my suit up. Well, I say wardrobe; it was a recess with a few coat hangers in it. The type of coat hangers you can't pinch. The type of coat hangers you can't get your suit jacket into. The type of coat hangers you end up hitting with your soft education consultant's fist like you're hitting somebody who's mugging you with their hard shelf-stacker's fists.

The coat hangers clattered like those annoying welcome bells that people used to hang over their doors. I laid my suit on the bed and the bloke next door shouted something indecipherable but angry through the cardboard-thin walls. I lifted two fingers in the air. I put them down.

I walked over to the window and looked out of room 624, the Great Houghton Welcome Inn, across to where the water park stretched towards the new road. June the 30th 2008; the first day of a two-day conference in the Welcome Inn's Barnsley Suite. 'Teaching Beyond History: Creative Responses to De-industrialisation for the Teacher of Key Stage 3.' I was proud of that title, proud of the way I'd stuck up for it at the meeting at the Teachers' Centre.

"It sounds too academic," Bill Foster had said, leaning closer as he tried to pluck a hair from his nose.

"That's the point, Bill" I said, almost smiling as he winced. "Because I think that we should emphasise the academic basis of what we're doing and the fact that Green Valley College is the first in the country to be doing such a thing."

He wasn't listening. He was too busy up his nose. Anyway, Channel 4 was too academic for him.

I eventually brought Bill and the rest of them round to my way of thinking about the title of the conference and most of the programme. It was harder, much harder, to convince them of the location. I said we should have it in the Dearne Valley, in an area that had totally transformed since I'd left nearly 20 years ago: pits shut, communities fragmented, collectivism smashed, call-centres rampant. They said that we could watch power point presentations and listen to speakers just as easily in London. I said that you needed to be there to get the full impact of the changes. They said we'd just be academic tourists hoovering up regeneration porn. I played my trump card: this was my home, and so I could take them to streets I knew, meet people who'd stayed and get them to talk firsthand about the changes in language that even Bill would understand, if he could make his way past what he called our 'Yorkshire brogue eee by gum, tha knows'.

Eventually they agreed, just to shut me up. The budget was no problem because the QCA were fully behind this new Beyond History A Level: they wanted to make it work. I wish they'd had Beyond Maths in my day.

So here I was in the thin-walled hotel they'd built on

the site of Houghton Main Pit, once one of the biggest mines in the region. Maybe that's why the wall of my room had a crack in it: shifting stones, shifting histories. Maybe I should have called the conference that. Maybe they hadn't really sealed the shaft and filled it in.

I went down to the breakfast room. Inevitably it was called The Lamp Room. I gave the kid my room number and he said:

"Will you be having the Pit Top breakfast or the Full Miner's, sir?"

I noticed that his badge told me he was Bradley and he was Happy To Help.

"Did your dad work down the pit?" I asked him.

He shook his head.

"I'm from Northampton. I just stayed on after my media studies course at the university."

He looked like he should have been in a boy band that only just made the second round of a TV talent show before they got voted off.

I plumped for the Full Miner's from the buffet and helped myself to three sausages even though each bite shortened my life by 37 minutes. I looked around the breakfast room, nodding at one or two of the other delegates, and for some reason I felt an odd kind of pride. I thought back to my parents, all those years ago, taking me to university, to a world they'd never understand, and now here I was, years later, divorced, bald, plump, and with a sad tattoo on my arse from an ill-advised stag weekend in Lodz, where the bloke couldn't even spell

Barnsley FC. Barnley. Somewhere between Burnley and Barnstaple and Hell. But also, here I was, organising a conference that would be the start of a new kind of history teaching, an A Level that included creative responses to history: stories, poems, songs, blogs, art. All history is interpretive anyway, so why not make it official?

I wondered whether or not I should have another sausage. Then I saw Buster Crabbe coming towards me. I decided I'd have two. Jimmy 'Buster' Crabbe, son of the late Doreen and Ernest Crabbe, stalwarts of the Co-operative Amateur Operatic Society, with the emphasis more on the amateur than the co-operative, if the reports of the AGMs in the *Barnsley Chronicle* were anything to go by. Doreen and Ernest, male and female shaky-voiced leads in everything from *White Horse Inn* to an ill advised production of *Hair* set in Wombwell Baths with the nudity replaced by swimming costumes.

Buster had inherited his parents' love of the limelight, although his was a rebellious style of showbiz from punk bands with names like The Vomit of St Paul to Barnsley's first experience of Street Theatre, which led to Buster, in a giant papier mache Margaret Thatcher's head, being dumped in a skip by some blokes on their way to the chip shop from a redundancy lump-sum spending party at the Gardener's Arms.

I'd got the name of his company from Google, then put two-and-two together and come up with the Co-op Amateur Ops. Buster, like the rest of us, had mellowed over the years. His only sign of rebellion nowadays was that one of his sideboards was longer than the other, although that may have been accidental. He still spoke pure Barnsley, though, as a reaction to his parents packing him off for elocution lessons with Mrs Golightly on Thomas Street.

I wanted Bill to be here, next to us by the sausages, to hear the social and cultural history that came out from between Buster's brown teeth every time he opened his mouth.

"Reyt" he said, leaning closer than I wanted him to. "Tha noz we're all theer, and tha noz wheer we're gunner kick off from ... "

I nodded. This was to be the conference's Coup de Theatre: a restaging of an incident in the Summer of 1984 when a group of riot police burst through some poor individual's house in Armthorpe in pursuit of a picket. Only this time Buster and his performance troupe The Flying Squad would rampage through our coffee break wearing police uniforms and with black tape over their serial numbers like authentic strike bobbies. This would bring home to my still-half-asleep delegates the power of responding to history creatively. Funny: Buster never left, even after his mam and dad had both died, she on a Celbrity cruise learning how to do fretwork, him bending over a cold frame on his allotment. He seemed to like being a huge fish in a pond, so small it was almost a patch of damp.

Buster was warming to his task:

"Duz tha reckon it'd be oreet if I gid one or two on 'em

a clip wi't baton? Just a tickle, like, but make it moor tha noz authentic in a manner of speyks ..."

I shook my head.

"Just wave the batons about, Buster. Just wave the batons about."

He nodded, disappointed, and wandered off. I finished my breakfast and went to the Barnsley suite to check that the flipcharts were ready to flip and the power point was powering up. The room was empty apart from a middle-aged bloke who was dishing out notepads to each table. I nodded to him. I expected the hotel's technical man would be in soon to check out the PA. The bloke carried on giving out the notebook and pens, pens that I'd pinch later on and put in the jar at home.

I looked at my watch: they should be getting the PA working by now. We were due to start soon. I went over to the hotel man who had finished doling out the stationery and was putting tiny mints into little bowls.

"Do you know when the PA technician's coming?" I asked. "Only we'll be needing it in about twenty minutes."

The man looked up and my heart skipped a beat. There was something about him, some vague memory tickling the back of my neck. He felt it to, on his neck, obviously, not mine. He stuck out his hand:

"It's Richard, isn't it?' he said, quietly.

Brian Scattergood! Good-for-Nowt Scattergood's youngest lad; Good-For-Nowt Scattergood, forever known as Scabbergood after he went back to work on a freezing morning in January 1985, his white face peeping out from behind the mesh on the bus windows like a fish looking through a keep net. After that he never got served in the club, nobody talked to him in the street, nobody would sit near him at Oakwell and he had to leave the area. Some said he'd changed his name and was living in Mold and there was a rumoured sighting on a ferry on the way to the Isle of Mull in a storm but nobody had seen him, really seen him, for years. The rest of the family had moved out too, couldn't stand the silences and the shit through the letterbox every January. Except Brian. He'd stayed, put up with the jeering and the bullying and just hung on. He was my age and I remember he almost went to university but his mam was bad on her legs and needed him to help her get to the commode, so that was that. And now here he was, giving out sweets.

"How you keeping, Brian?" I asked.

The sun flooded through the windows.

"Not bad," he said, a South Yorkshire phrase that covered a spectrum of meaning.

The room fell silent except for the sound of Brian dropping sweets into dishes.

"My dad's dead, you know."

"I'm sorry. I didn't know."

"This place killed him. He never wanted to go back to work, but how else could he put food on the table?'

Lots of other people were in the same boat but they didn't go back to work, I thought — but didn't speak. It was strange, this, coming back to the place that had nurtured me and made me who I was and listening to somebody talking about it with such bitterness. Mind you, I'd scuttled away; he was here. Brian gestured to the carpet. I thought he'd dropped a sweet.

"That's where the cage was," he said.

I didn't know what he was on about. I gazed at the floor.

"The shaft was here. We're standing on the shaft, and the cage went down here ... "

Ah, the pit cage, zooming men down to the face faster than any lift you'd ever been in, like a plane coming down to land too quickly, far too quickly.

"That's where my dad went. That's where he went into the dark."

Brian's eyes were bright with tears. Surreptitiously I picked up a pen like I needed one and clicked it into my top pocket. Then I got another. Brian chucked the last few sweets onto the table and walked out of the room.

As he left he almost bumped into a bunch of the delegates who were coming in. What about the PA? I could see the microphones were there, and the speakers, too big for the room like speakers at a wedding disco. A lad came in wearing a hotel jacket. It was Bradley from the breakfast room, the media studies student made good. He strode over to the microphone on the desk and switched it on. He did the same to the one on the lectern. He went to the back of the room and switched on a mixing desk. The room reverberated with feedback and I swear I heard some glasses shatter. Bradley pressed something and the torture ended.

"Sorry," he said.

He put his thumb up. I put my thumb up; Richard and Bradley, thumbs united by the joys of learning.

The conference started. I stood at the front and welcomed people, told them where the toilets were, told them we weren't expecting a fire drill, told them that if there was a fire bell they should go to clearly marked exits and they should follow me because I'd be going faster than shit off a red hot shovel. Nobody laughed. Somebody coughed.

I went to the lectern to deliver my Keynote Speech. It set out my thesis about learning history through creativity. I told them why we were here and not in some conference centre in the south, because I could tell them stories about the place, stories that reflected the wider sweep of history in the 50-odd years I'd been alive.

I told them about Harry and Jud, the gay cross-dressing couple who kept the shop that's now a museum, about the night in the Falklands War when Barnsley got promoted and HMS Sheffield sunk, about the benefit gigs that were almost a cultural arm of the miners' strike. It went down well. I got warm applause. People had taken notes, had looked at my CV on the conference brochure, had turned to each other and nodded.

It was coffee time. Time for the big event. Time for Buster Crabbe and his troupe to burst in and recreate a moment from 1984, to exemplify the kind of thing we were talking about. I stood near the door, a little nervously. People came up to congratulate me on my speech and I smiled and nodded. People finished their coffee and began to take their seats ready for the next speaker, an academic from the university who was talking about popular song as a reflection of cultural change. He'd got a guitar. With stickers on. Where was flaming Buster? I looked out of the door into the corridor. Nothing. Then I saw him. Buster, dressed as a copper, staggering along the corridor holding his face. I noticed his nose was bleeding. He was laughing.

"What the hell happened?" I asked.

"Bloody referees!" he said, indistinctly.

"What are you on about?"

"Went in the wrong conference. Yorkshire Rugby Referees AGM ...'

I must have looked shocked. He dabbed at his nose with his hankie. He smiled:

"Mind you, we gave as good as we got."

Behind him, I could see Brian Scattergood leading a fat bloke in a suit out of the Wombwell Suite. In the Barnsley Suite I could hear the delegates getting restless. Outside I could hear police and ambulance sirens getting louder and more urgent. Now where was that cage?

# Pomona backlist

Pomona is a wholly independent publisher dedicated to bringing before the public the work of prodigiously talented writers. Our books can be purchased on-line at:

www.pomonauk.co.uk


## FOOTNOTE*

Boff Whalley

ISBN 1-904590-00-4


*Footnote\** is clever, funny and irreverent—a story about a boy from the redbrick clichés of smalltown England reconciling Mormonism and punk rock, industrial courtesy and political insurrection.

He finds a guitar, anarchism and art terrorism and, after years (and years and years) of earnest, determined, honest-to-goodness slogging, his pop group† makes it big; that's BIG with a megaphone actually. They write a song that has the whole world singing and, funnily enough, it's an admirable summary of a life well lived—about getting knocked down and getting back up again.

Meanwhile, there's a whole world still happening: authentic lives carefully drawn, emotional but not sentimental and always with a writer's eye for detail. *Footnote* is not another plodding rock memoir but a compassionate, critical and sometimes cynical account of a life steeped in pop culture, lower division football and putting the world to rights.

---

\* See page 293 of Boff Whalley's book.
† Boff Whalley is a member of Chumbawamba.

# RULE OF NIGHT

Trevor Hoyle

ISBN 1-904590-01-2

If the Sixties were swinging, the Seventies were the hangover —
darker, nastier, uglier — especially if you lived on a council estate in
the north of England.

*Rule of Night* was first published in 1975 and has since become a
cult classic. It pre-dates the current vogue for 'hard men' and 'football
hoolie' books by 25 years.

It is, however, much more than this. Trevor Hoyle creates a chill-
ingly detailed world, where teenagers prowl rainy fluorescent-lit
streets dressed as their *Clockwork Orange* anti-heroes. The backdrop
is provided by Ford Cortinas, Players No.6, the factory, the relentless
struggle to maintain hope.

Hoyle, who has since been published by John Calder (home to
Samuel Beckett and William S. Burroughs), has added a fascinating
afterword to his original book which has been out of print and highly
sought-after for many years.

# THE FAN

## Hunter Davies

ISBN 1-904590-02-0

Hunter Davies is one of Britain's most acclaimed writers and journalists. He has written over 30 books, among them modern classics, *The Beatles* and *A Walk Around The Lakes*. *The Glory Game*, published in 1972, is a benchmark work on football and is still in print today.

*The Fan* is a collection of very personal, unusual pieces about his life as a supporter. He observes football in its sovereignty of the late 1900s and early 2000s and tackles the big topics of the day: Beckham's haircuts, high finance, the price of pies, the size of match day programmes, the enormous wages, the influence of Sky TV, England's numerous managers.

Along the way, he also lets us into his home life, in London and the Lake District, his family, his work, his tortoise, his poorly knee (caused by too much Sunday football).

Originally published in the *New Statesman* magazine, *The Fan* catches Davies at his very best and most amusing. It will appeal to supporters of any age, sex and loyalties.

# LOVE SONGS

## Crass

ISBN 1-904590-03-9

> *Our love of life is total,*
> *everything we do is an expression of that.*
> *Everything that we write is a love song.*
>
> – Penny Rimbaud, *Yes, Sir, I Will*

CRASS: a rural collective based in Essex, formed in 1977 of a diverse and eclectic group of individuals who operated for several years using music, art, literature and film as vehicles to share information and ideas. They also wanted to change the world.

This is a collection of words spanning those seven short years; a book of shock slogans and mindless token tantrums. An anthology of passionate love songs that sought to inspire a generation, and succeeded.

# SUM TOTAL

Ray Gosling

ISBN 1-904590-05-5

*Sum Total* is a lost masterpiece of British literature, a restless, hungry riposte to America's finest Beat writers.

Written in 1961 when he was just 21, Gosling's itchy 'sort of' autobiography is a startlingly original take on the England of the early Sixties: rock 'n' roll, trains, dead-end jobs, drizzle, hitchhiking, jukebox cafés, trudging through hometown streets.

All the time he remains gloriously indulgent, disillusioned yet hopeful, tired but desperate for every new day.

Although now famous for hundreds of television and radio documentaries, in *Sum Total* Gosling reveals himself as a writer years ahead of his time, presenting a skew-whiff, arch and droll view of the world, both inside and out.

He has added a typically idiosyncratic and lengthy preface to the original text.

# DIARY OF A HYPERDREAMER

Bill Nelson

ISBN 1-904590-06-3

Bill Nelson is one of Britain's most respected creative forces. He came to prominence in the Seventies with Be Bop Deluxe and later Red Noise. He has collaborated with like-minds such as Yellow Magic Orchestra, David Sylvian, Harold Budd and Roger Eno and still releases a prolific amount of new music.

*Diary of a Hyperdreamer* is his day-by-day journal in which he ponders on life, art and the nation. His unique perspective is fed by a career creating and producing music, photography, painting and video.

Written from his home in a hamlet in north Yorkshire, he also includes engaging details of his family life, regular musings on mortality, along with reflections on his childhood and former life as a globe-trotting 'pop star.'

# THE PRICE OF COAL

## Barry Hines

ISBN 1-904590-08-X

Barry Hines is a master craftsman. While he is rightly celebrated for his classic, *A Kestrel for a Knave* (later filmed as *Kes*), his other work is equally powerful.

*The Price of Coal* is an uncompromising depiction of life at a colliery where beer, snooker, cricket and time spent on the allotment is the only respite from clawing coal from the earth.

A royal visit prompts the introduction of soft soap to the toilets, grass seeds scattered on the slag heap, and lashings of white paint across the site.

But when disaster strikes the superficial is forgotten as men fight for their lives in the darkness underneath collapsing seams of coal.

As ever, Hines proves himself an exemplary storyteller with a discerning eye for detail and when bolder, gaudier writing is long forgotten, his stays in the mind and nourishes it.

He has written a new foreword to the original text which was first published in 1979 and later adapted for television as two linked plays, directed by Ken Loach in the acclaimed *Play for Today* series.

# LOOKS & SMILES

Barry Hines

ISBN 1-904590-09-8

*Looks and Smiles* is a lost bulletin from the early-Eighties when the sun felt to have set permanently on hope and optimism. Unemployment was rampant, especially in the north where traditional industries were laid waste by Margaret Thatcher and her government.

Set amid this gloom, *Looks and Smiles* is an under-stated love affair between unemployed school-leaver Mick and Karen who works in a town centre shoe shop. They both want little more from life than a decent chance.

As ever, Hines proves himself an exemplary storyteller with a discerning eye for detail. He never resorts to sentimentality, and hope, however slender, flickers always.

The book was originally published in 1981 and later made into a film by Ken Loach.

# KICKED INTO TOUCH (PLUS EXTRA-TIME)
## Fred Eyre

ISBN 1-904590-12-8

Fred Eyre's sporting life began full of promise when he became Manchester City's first ever apprentice. He never made their first team. In fact, he seldom made anyone's first team. Injuries played a part but limited talent was the greater curse. As he plummeted down the leagues he had something few footballers possess: a stud-sharp memory and an ability to write humorously about the sport he loves.

Originally published in 1981, *Kicked Into Touch* has become an enigma —selling more than a million copies yet still retaining cult status within the sport and among fans. This new version has been completely revised, extended and updated with a new set of photographs included.

It is set to reach a new generation of football fans looking for an antidote to the glib reportage of a sport lost to show business.

# MEAN WITH MONEY

Hunter Davies

ISBN 1-904590-13-6

At last, a book about money that tells it straight: put it under the bed. All of it. Sure, it makes for easy access to burglars but better them than the felons passing themselves off as financial advisors or acting as foot-soldiers for organisations with words like union, mutual, trust, alliance, equitable or assurance in their name.

*Mean With Money*, inspired by Hunter Davies' well-loved column in *The Sunday Times*, is wilfully short on practical advice but offers instead good humour and much-needed empathy as we face the corporate horror of high-handed and indifferent financial institutions.

Davies, one of Britain's most celebrated writers, also looks at ingenious ways to save money (cut your own hair, for starters) and what to do with it when it arrives. Along the way, he reveals details of his regular visits to McDonald's (it's free to use their toilets), the eccentric old ladies who staff his local Oxfam shop and the swim that cost him £333.

Famous for seminal works on The Beatles, football, and subjects as diverse as lottery winners and walking disused railway tracks, Davies is, once more, on top form. Go get 'em Hunt.

# ZONE OF THE INTERIOR

Clancy Sigal

ISBN 1-904590-10-1

'The book they dared not print', *Zone of the Interior* is a lost classic of zonked-out, high-as-a-kite Sixties literature. It tells the story of Sid Bell, an American political fugitive in London, who falls under the spell of Dr. Willie Last (partly modelled on the radical 'anti-psychiatrist' RD Laing). This unlikely duo feast on LSD, mescaline, psilocybin and psycho-babble, believing that only by self-injecting themselves with schizophrenia will they become true existentialist guerrillas. Their 'purple haze' odyssey takes them into the eye of the hurricane — mental hospitals, secure units for the violent, the Harley Street cabal of the 'Sacred 7' and semi-derelict churches that come complete with an underground tank for the woman convinced she's a fish. Sigal's approach is richly sardonic and anti-establishment, of both right and left, in a jazz-influenced free-form prose, comic and serious, myth-puncturing and elegiac. Along the way Sigal, now an established Hollywood screen-writer, makes the case for a revolutionary period of mental health nursing whose task is as yet undone.

# THE ARMS OF THE INFINITE

Christopher Barker

ISBN 1-904590-04-7

Christopher Barker is the son of the cult writer Elizabeth Smart (*By Grand Central Station I Sat Down and Wept*) and the notorious poet, George Barker.

*The Arms of the Infinite* takes the reader inside the minds of both parents and, from their first fateful meeting and subsequent elopement, Barker candidly reveals their obsessive, passionate and volatile love affair.

He writes evocatively of his unconventional upbringing with his siblings in a shack in Ireland and, later, a rambling, falling-down house in Essex. Interesting and charismatic figures from the literary and art worlds are regular visitors and the book is full of fascinating cameos and anecdotes.

Barker is himself a gifted writer. An early draft of his memoir formed a cover story for the literary magazine, *Granta*.

# THE SECOND HALF

Hunter Davies

ISBN 1-904590-14-4

*The Second Half* is another collection of personal pieces from the *New Statesman* covering the past three domestic seasons; the Euro Championship of 2004; and the 2006 World Cup when he unexpectedly became Wayne Rooney's top buddy.

'When a player gets sent off shouldn't we fans get some of our money back?' ponders Davies in one piece. 'I just wish he'd shave his stupid face,' he berates José Mourhino in another. And, goooaaal!, Hunt rumbles Sven early doors: 'He's a spare swede at a veggie gathering. What is the point of him?' he writes two years before England's World Cup debacle.

As ever, his outlook is fiercely that of the fan—disgruntled, bewildered and passionate—wondering what the players do with all that money, all those girls, and why match programmes are 'full of adverts or arse-licks for sponsors.'

And, finally, why did Peter Crouch? Because he saw Darren Bent, of course.

# BELIEVE IN THE SIGN

Mark Hodkinson

ISBN 1-904590-17-9

*Believe in the Sign* is about a damp corner of England where nothing much but everything happens. It is a 'sort of' memoir of a normal, average boy who would have grown up happily average and normal but for a dark and perverse passion: the seductive lure of masochistic devotion to a no-hope, near-derelict football club.

But it isn't all joyously uplifting. Swimming through the murk is a swarm of snapshots that bring growing up in the 1970s and 1980s into startling focus. Mad kids and sad kids and good kids from broken homes; teenage wrecking parties; pub brawls; long existential marches along the motorway banking; the baiting of Elton John and a club chairman caught playing 'away from home.'

Then Death bumps into Life. A girl is abducted and the town becomes a cave, the light sucked out. Meanwhile in the sunny shine outside, the future is afoot: cotton mills close down and supermarkets invade; school-leavers evolve into YOP-fodder and everyone's mum is holding Tupperware parties to get the down-payment on a colour telly.

Variously serious and funny, steely-eyed and tender, Hodkinson plumbs the depths but isn't afraid of the shallows. Dip a toe.

# THE NOT DEAD

Simon Armitage

ISBN 978-1-904-59018-7

"*The Not Dead* is uniquely impressive. In transmuting the stories of particular soldiers into the lyrical music of Simon Armitage's poems, something exceptional is achieved: the painful truth of lives damaged beyond help is made meaningful for the rest of us. We can only catch our breath and read them again and again."

– Joan Bakewell

# THIS ARTISTIC LIFE

Barry Hines

ISBN 978-1-904590-22-4

An anthology of essays and stories by Barry Hines, the author of the much-celebrated *A Kestrel for a Knave*, better known as *Kes*.

Many of the pieces were written at the same time as this seminal novel and have never been published before.

They cover Hines' love of sport along with his reflections on his home town of Hoyland Common, near Barnsley, both its landscape and the colourful characters that people it.

✷

# THE LAST MAD SURGE OF YOUTH

Mark Hodkinson

ISBN 978-1-904590-20-0

"A good group isn't about everyone being able to play well. You need people to shape it, give it heart. The best bands, the ones that matter, are a group of people singing about their lives, their mams and dads, the streets they came from, the crap jobs they've had, everything. And serving it all up pure to the public, saying, 'This is what we are — do you recognise any of it?' All the better if you were dragged up because punters see a kind of glamour in squalor. Ideally they'd like you to have been brought up by wolves, living half wild on the streets. That's what rock'n'roll is, why bands from these shitty estates get to be massive. And do you know why people like all this? It's because they're envious but rooting for you at the same time. Their own gang — the kids they grew up with – didn't stick together. They see you as someone who made it through and they want to be part of it. That's why they buy the records. It reminds them of what could have been."

*The Last Mad Surge of Youth* is an intelligent, literate work that sidesteps the usual clichés of rock novels. Its authenticity and authority is never compromised, a viewpoint held dear by punk and new wave. It is also about growing up, friendship, fame, addiction, love. And hope.